G000294296

FOREST MERLINS IN SCOTLAND
Their Requirements and Management

A report on
THE GALLOWAY FORESTS MERLIN PROJECT
(1986-89)

by
Jack Orchel

With illustrations by
Donald Watson and John Haywood

" Merlins are very easily overlooked in their breeding and winter haunts, so that when the species is properly investigated it may be found to be more common than I fear it may be. I hope so, for this is a splendid little bird, quite inoffensive to man, yet possessing all the fire and the dash of the peregrine."

Leslie Brown 1976

The Hawk and Owl Trust
London

Copyright © by Jacek Henryk Orchel 1992.
First published 1992 by
The Hawk and Owl Trust
c/o Zoological Society of London
Regent's Park, London NW1 4RY.
Design and computer graphics
by the author.

Produced for the Hawk and Owl Trust
by May, Winfield & Associates Ltd
Greenwich, London SE10 9JB.

All rights reserved.

ISBN 0 9503187 4 4

Keywords : Birds, Merlin, *Falco columbarius*, Forestry, Moorland, Scotland.

British Library Cataloguing-in-Publication Data.
A Catalogue record for this book is available
from the British Library.

The Hawk and Owl Trust wishes to acknowledge the special contribution made
by the Country Landowners' Association towards this project and expresses its
gratitude to Jupiter Tarbutt Merlin Ltd and the V & S Charitable Trust for
helping to meet the costs of printing this report.

CONTENTS

LIST OF PHOTOGRAPHS

All photgraphs without credits were taken by the author.

LIST OF FIGURES

LIST OF TABLES

Drumlanrig Castle, Thornhill, Scotland, DG3 4AQ

FOREWORD

This detailed and thorough work was inspired by the author's discovery of a Merlin nest in a tall Sitka spruce within a mature forest in Galloway in 1982 when many ornithologists were greatly concerned about the decline of the Merlin and the loss of its traditional nesting places in deep heather due to afforestation. In the best tradition of British scholarship, this independent report draws on the expertise of foresters, rangers and wildlife managers of both private forests and the Forestry Commission working in close partnership with the Hawk and Owl Trust over a period of several years. The Country Landowners' Association have been staunch supporters of this project, backing Jack Orchel's scientific and historical research as a basis for practical guidelines for conservation of the Merlin and its breeding habitat in British forests.

This report makes a very important contribution to the study of Merlins in Scotland. It reveals that the species is capable of adapting to changing land use in our uplands and can at least stabilise its numbers and hopefully recover, if undisturbed, in well planned forests where a mosaic of moorland habitat is retained to allow the bird to continue to hunt successfully. I am particularly pleased to write this foreword as my family has, for over 500 years, managed a considerable part of South West Scotland, where the main study has taken place. A report of this kind will surely lead to greater knowledge and understanding of this delightful and popular little bird, known locally as the "wee blue falcon".

I hope that the creative wildlife management guidelines in this publication will commend themselves to all country lovers, including foresters, so that more wildlife managers can be employed in the private sector, perhaps with the help of government and EEC incentives, leading to a recovery in Merlin numbers and ensuring the future of the species, not only in Scotland but elsewhere in Britain's uplands.

The Duke of Buccleuch & Queensberry, K.T.

To Pauline and Katie
without whose patience, understanding, encouragement and help
this study would not have been completed.

Special Dedication

This publication is dedicated to the memory of John Haywood (1936-1991), falconer, wildlife artist and friend of the Hawk and Owl Trust since its foundation in 1969 and also to the memory of Stephen Murphy (1964 -1990) who loved birds of prey.

AUTHOR'S ACKNOWLEDGEMENTS

This report is the product of a collaborative study of birds of prey in the coniferous forests of south-west Scotland. The Galloway Forests Merlin Project was initiated by Richard Grant-Rennick, Vice-President of the Hawk and Owl Trust and was approved in 1985 by the Forestry Commission's Conservator for South Scotland, David L Foot, who recognised the need for a Merlin census in the western Southern Uplands. John Livingstone (FC Conservancy Wildlife Officer 1980-92) was subsequently assigned to work with me to coordinate raptor surveys by the Commission's forest ranger team. It is largely thanks to his enthusiasm, efficient liaison with forest managers, rangers and the Trust, his extensive knowledge of the region's wildlife and commitment to sensitive raptor management in productive forests, that this project proved successful. I am very grateful for his cooperation and also wish to express my appreciation to John Ogilvie who, as Private Forestry and Environment Officer, supervised this conservation initiative on Forestry Commission lands.

It is a great pleasure to acknowledge the support offered by Willie Mitchell, General Manager (Borders Division) of Economic Forestry Group PLC, who allowed his professional wildlife managers led by Ronnie Rose Sr MBE to participate in the project. For granting access to their estates in South Scotland and for encouraging their keepers to record Merlin sightings I thank the Duke of Buccleuch and Queensberry KT and the Earl of Dalkeith. Special thanks are also due to the management of Fountain Forestry Ltd, in particular to Mike Ashmole, George McRobbie, Dick Repton and Ranald Lamb, for involving their forest rangers in this study. I am grateful for the help and access to land offered by Ron J Smith, Regional Manager of Scottish Woodlands, Mike Jackson and Alister Menarry of Lambert-Jackson, Richard Kay of David Goss and Associates, the owners of Glenapp and Lagafater estates and the managers of Tilhill Forestry Ltd.

My sincere thanks go to the large team of fieldworkers who completed raptor survey booklets in 1986-87; without their diligence and expertise this report could not have been prepared :

Forestry Commission

Steven Brazendale	Ronald Creevy	Callum Ferguson
Ian Fergusson	Samuel K Fergusson	Hugh Gunning
Robin Heaney	Barry Holiday	Willie Laurie
John Livingstone	John MacDonald	Louis McCleary
Frank McGhie	Andrew McMahon	Donald McPhail
Ian Murray	Jim Newall	Robert Ryman
Geoff Shaw	Ron Steele	Graham Todd
Ian Watret	Ian White	Roy White

Economic Forestry Group

Ronnie Rose Sr	Peter Kirk	John Wykes

Fountain Forestry

Jim Campbell	Gordon Frizzell	Jim Whitby

Lambert Jackson — Alister Menarry

Scottish Woodlands — Jock Smith — Gordon Wykes

Tilhill Forestry — Robert W Armstrong — Jim Ferguson

Gamekeepers — Donald Anderson — Jim Bissett

Ornithologists

Tuer Holm	David Callan	John Edwards
Norman Pool	Richard Pickup	Jean Pool
	Ron Scott	

For offering assistance, encouragement and administrative support I thank the following employees of the Forestry Commission : Richard Britton, Colin Brookes, Tony Burns, Gordon M Cowie, Graham Gill, Jim Hamilton, Alastair T Jones, Roderick Leslie, Colin Phillipson, Ernie Meechie, Steve Petty, Phil Ratcliffe, Tony Lewis, Bill Thomson and Irving Walker. Especial thanks are due to John Davies, former FC Conservator (S.Scotland), for allowing me to commence my studies of birds of prey in the Galloway Forest Park fifteen years ago.

I am indebted to Donald Watson whose wash drawings greatly enhance this publication. Copies of his Galloway Merlin records spanning more than twenty years were kindly made available to me as were extracts from the unpublished writings of Wigtownshire naturalist Jack G Gordon. Further retrospective Merlin records were received from Derek Ratcliffe and John Theaker of the Nature Conservancy Council as well as from Jack Henderson, Charles Park and Alex Russell.

The following Merlin researchers furnished details of their studies, considerably broadening my horizons : Dale Becker (Montana), Colin Bibby (Wales), Keith Hodson (Alberta & Saskatchewan), Lynn Oliphant (Saskatchewan), Philip Schempf (Alaska), Larry Toal (Northern Ireland) and Eric Meek, Dave Okill, Sandy Payne and Graham Rebecca (Scotland). My thanks are also extended to Stephen Baillie, Humphrey Crick, David Gibbons and Chris Mead of the British Trust for Ornithology for responding positively to requests for data. My appreciation also to Denise Reed, Alison Roberts, Nick Picozzi and Howard Swann who provided helpful background information for this report. Additional data and advice were kindly offered by the following : Robin Ade, Gordon Bevan, Alan Brooks, Mike Callan, John Cooper, Paul Denton, Andrew Duncan, Neil Forbes, Peter Hudson, Leonard Hurrell, Terry I'Anson, David Jardine, Mick Marquiss, Ronnie Rose Jr, Chris Ross, Dick Roxburgh and the head keepers of the Buccleuch Estates (John Cotts, Ronald Gibson, Brian Johnson and Brian Mitchell). My thanks to Paul Quarmby for statistical analysis of the moorland habitat data and to Roy Blewitt, Mike Callan, Dennis Green, Graham Rebecca and Brian Turner for providing splendid Merlin photographs for this publication. For locating scientific papers at short notice I am grateful to the librarians at Alice Holt Lodge, NCC Peterborough and Edinburgh, the Institute Of Terrestrial Ecology at Banchory, the Zoological Society of London and the Department of Ornithology of the Natural History Museum, Tring.

It is with sincere gratitude that I acknowledge the time and effort devoted to this project by my colleagues in the Hawk and Owl Trust : President - Lord John Tweedsmuir CBE; Vice-President - Richard Grant-Rennick; Chairmen - Anthony Boosey, Jane Fenton, Georgina Harding; Vice-Chairmen - David Cobham, Philip Burton; Trustees - Russell Coope, Howard Swann; Committee Member - Roger Clarke; also Valerie Shawyer. Warmest thanks go to the Director of the Trust, Colin Shawyer, who was associated with every stage of the project, from preparation of the first survey booklet to offering valuable criticisms of the final report and supervising its publication. I owe much to Lord Tweedsmuir, Jane Fenton and Georgina Harding for promoting the Trust's work in Scotland.

For their constructive comments on earlier drafts of this document I wish to thank Roger Clarke, Russell Coope, Roderick Leslie, John Ogilvie, Geoff Shaw and Donald Watson. I am also indebted to Richard Britton, John Livingstone, George McRobbie, Willie Mitchell, John Phillips, Ronnie Rose Sr and Christina Tracey whose suggestions improved the Merlin conservation guidelines.

Finally, on behalf of the Hawk and Owl Trust, I would like to thank the Country Landowners' Association for supporting this project so generously.

1   INTRODUCTION

The diminutive Merlin *Falco columbarius* is a scarce predatory bird which breeds in the uplands of Britain and Ireland. Traditionally known in Britain as "the moorland falcon", the species is specially adapted to catch avian prey in open and semi-open habitats (Temple 1972, Bengtson 1975, Trimble 1975, Cade 1982). It is listed in Annex 1 of the European Community Directive on the Conservation of Wild Birds (79/409/EEC) among those species which **"shall be the subject of special conservation measures concerning their habitat in order to ensure their survival and reproduction in their area of distribution."** Whilst Merlins winter in France, Spain and other European countries, within the European Community itself they only breed in Scotland, England, Ireland and Wales.

In the United Kingdom, under the Wildlife and Countryside Act 1981 and the Wildlife (Northern Ireland) Order 1985, the Merlin is afforded special protection against persecution as well as wilful disturbance at or near the nest. However, because Merlins have large hunting ranges and since more than 90% of UK Merlins are thought to breed outside designated sites such as National Nature Reserves and Sites of Special Scientific Interest, conservation of the species' breeding habitat is almost totally dependent on two factors : a) UK Government policies for the wider countryside and b) the farming, forestry and sporting interests of private landowners.

Although some leading ornithologists still consider the British Merlin population to be declining and locally threatened by habitat loss and possibly toxic chemical contamination (Batten *et al.* 1990, Crick *in press*), the advent of environmentally sensitive agriculture and forestry policies provides an unprecedented opportunity to safeguard strongholds of this species. The situation is particularly favourable in Scotland where Indicative Forest Strategies form an integral part of the Regional Structure Plans which are being developed as a general framework for future land use and resource management; moreover, a number of Environmentally Sensitive Areas have already been established and several more proposed in the Scottish uplands to promote conservation-friendly farming practices and preservation of semi-natural habitats and their fauna (Highland Regional Council 1989, Strathclyde Regional Council 1990, Borders Regional Council 1991, Galbraith & Bates 1991, DAFS 1989, Scottish Office 1992, Appendix 9).

Of the four species of falcon - Peregrine, Kestrel, Hobby and Merlin - which breed in the British Isles, the last is by far the most elusive. Although Merlins are known to nest repeatedly in the same general area over several years and return to a previously used area after a period of absence (Bibby 1986), they tend to use a selection of alternative sites, spread over distances up to 2 km apart (Ratcliffe 1990). This tendency and their habit of sitting very tight when on eggs and brooding small chicks make it difficult to census breeding pairs, particularly in forested districts (Petty 1985b, Little & Davison 1992).

A national survey of the species, coordinated by the Royal Society for the Protection of Birds (RSPB) in the years 1983-84, located 375 breeding pairs and estimated the British population to be 550-650 pairs including about 300 pairs in Scotland. Relatively high densities (typically 3-5 pairs/100 km^2) were found in some upland areas dominated by heather managed as grouse moor (Bibby and Nattrass 1986). The RSPB survey identified moorland strongholds of the Merlin in parts of northern England, north and north-east Scotland and Wales; however, this important study provided only minimal coverage of the many thousands of kilometres of suitable, coniferous forest-edge, breeding habitat in the uplands of these countries and so the British population estimate quoted above must be viewed as conservative. Today there may indeed be about 800 breeding pairs in Britain including 60-100 pairs in Wales and 350-400 pairs in Scotland, judging by the results of recent searches (Parr *in press*, Benn 1991). A further 100-150 pairs could well breed in Ireland where the bird is widespread and regularly nests in woodland (Hutchinson 1989).

In order to gain an insight into how Merlins are utilising forest habitats the Hawk and Owl Trust in association with the Forestry Commission and several forest management companies conducted a raptor survey during 1986 and 1987 in part of south-west Scotland, considered to be the most extensively afforested region in the British Isles (Avery & Leslie 1990, Figure 5). Follow-up studies took place within and outside this area between 1988 and 1991.

This report reviews historical information about Merlins in south-west Scotland, examines habitat preferences of forest-nesting pairs and presents Merlin conservation guidelines for use by foresters in the region. General conservation guidelines are also included to assist forest and estate managers in other parts of Scotland where Merlins are already nesting in maturing conifer plantations and where new forests may be established near traditional moorland nesting areas.

In this report, the term "forest" refers not merely to woodland but includes all unplanted land within the forest estate.

2   BASIC ECOLOGY OF THE MERLIN

2.1   DESCRIPTION

By comparison with most raptors the European Merlin *Falco columbarius aesalon* is a small, compact bird. The larger, dark brown female weighs about 220 grams or 7.5 ounces (range 220-270 grams during incubation) whereas the blue-grey male weighs nearer 160 grams or 5.5 ounces (range 160-170 grams during the breeding season) (Newton *et al.* 1984). Fledged juveniles resemble the adult female in plumage. From head to tail Merlins measure only 25-30 centimetres (10-12 inches). Equipped with relatively long, pointed wings and a wingspan of 50-62 cm (20-25 inches), they are capable of extremely rapid flight and great aerial agility (Cramp & Simmons 1980). Birds similar in size and colouring to the darker and slightly larger, Icelandic race *Falco columbarius subaesalon* are known to breed in northern England and Scotland (Robertson 1982, Picozzi 1983).

2.2   GENERAL DISTRIBUTION AND NESTING HABITS

Merlins are breeding birds of northern Holarctic distribution, ranging from subarctic to temperate regions. They are essentially birds of the forest edge and occur throughout North America, Northern Europe, North and Central Asia, "wherever forests and scrublands are extensively broken by expanses of open country" (Cade 1982, p.114). There are nine subspecies of which three are found in N. America, two in N. Europe and four east of the Caspian Sea and Ural Mountains in the former Soviet Union (Temple 1972, Dementiev & Gladkov 1951). Merlins nest at the northern and southern margins of the boreal forest zone in association with tundra in the north and grasslands (prairies/steppes) in the south. Within the boreal forest or taiga they nest near lakes, along wide river valleys and close to large openings created by forest fires and bogs (Lawrence 1949, Dementiev & Gladkov 1951, Beebe 1974, Cramp & Simmons 1980, Galushin 1981, Cade 1982). They also nest near the timberline in mountainous regions of North America, Fenno-Scandia and Central Asia (Laing 1985, Wiklund 1977, Kovshar & Rodionov 1984).

Unlike the accipiters, falcons do not build a nest but frequently lay their eggs in a scrape on the ground. In Iceland (as is the case in part of Sutherland) Merlins nest on vegetated cliff ledges and steep vegetated slopes (Nielsen 1986, Thompson *et al.* 1989); elsewhere at the Arctic treeline ground nests beneath shrubs are not uncommon (Bent 1938, Trimble 1975, Ritchie 1983) but throughout the rest of their range Merlins generally nest in coniferous and deciduous trees, utilising old stick nests of other species, particularly those of Magpie, American Crow and Hooded Crow (Fox 1964, Hodson 1976, Olsson 1980, Galushin 1981, Becker & Sieg 1987, Schempf & Titus 1988). In recent years this behaviour has enabled Richardson's Merlin *Falco columbarius richardsonii* to colonise urban centres on the Canadian prairies where maturing, planted conifers have provided abundant nest sites for American Crows and where House Sparrows in urban areas and on nearby farms are a dependable source of food for Merlins throughout the year (Oliphant 1974, Oliphant & McTaggart 1977, Smith 1978, Oliphant & Haug 1985, James & Smith 1987, James 1988, Warkentin & James 1988, Warkentin & Oliphant 1990, Warkentin *et al.* 1991).

2.3 BREEDING DISTRIBUTION IN BRITAIN

In Britain, Merlins nest from the windswept Shetland Isles in northern Scotland (60°40'N, 10°W) to the moors of south-west England (51°5'N, 3°40'W), the southern limit of their breeding range in western Europe. They occupy a variety of habitats in upland landscapes highly modified by man, where natural vegetative succession has been arrested by centuries of tree felling, burning and grazing (Ritchie 1920, Weir 1984, Ratcliffe & Thompson 1988). It is not surprising, therefore, that of 424 nests recorded by Bibby and Nattrass in 1983 and 1984, 324 (76%) were ground nests mainly situated in rank heather. The breeding range of the species in Britain closely resembles the distribution of upland habitats i.e. areas above the upper limit of enclosed land (Ratcliffe 1977) presented in Figure 1. The main breeding areas in Scotland are shown in Figure 2.

Today in parts of Ireland, Wales, northern England and Scotland where tracts of semi-natural vegetation (grasslands, dwarf-shrub heaths and grazed blanket bogs) have been converted to plantation forest, mainly over the past thirty years (Figure 1b), the Merlin is already a tree-nesting bird of the forest margins (Newton *et al.* 1986a, Hutchinson 1989, C J Bibby, A Brooks, P Kirk, S J Petty, L Toal (pers. comm.), Batten *et al.* 1990, Parr 1991, Scott *et al.* 1991, Little & Davison 1992, Rebecca 1992).

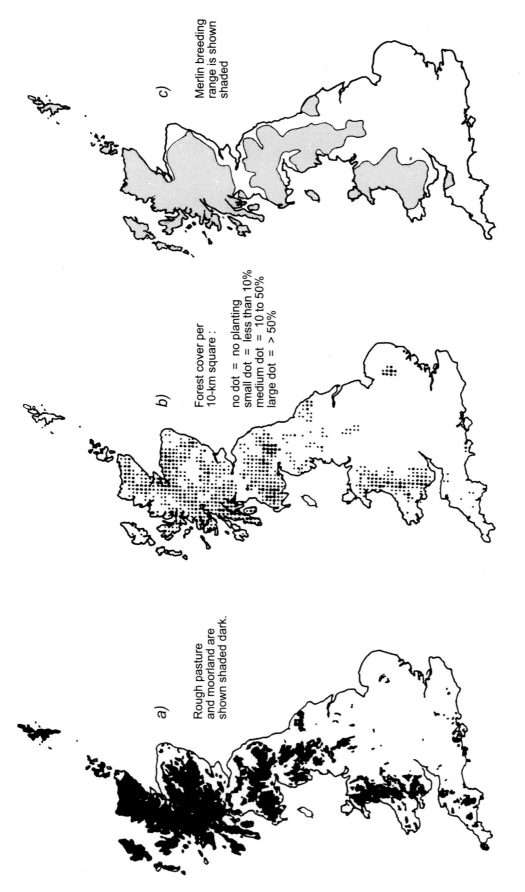

Figure 1. Distribution of a) upland habitats (rough pasture and moorland), b) existing forest (as in 1986) planted since 1920 in every 10-km square of the National Grid and c) breeding range of the Merlin in Britain in 1988-1991. (Sources : NCC 1986; Gibbons et al. in press.)

a)

Rough pasture and moorland are shown shaded dark.

b)

Forest cover per 10-km square :

no dot = no planting
small dot = less than 10%
medium dot = 10 to 50%
large dot = > 50%

c)

Merlin breeding range is shown shaded

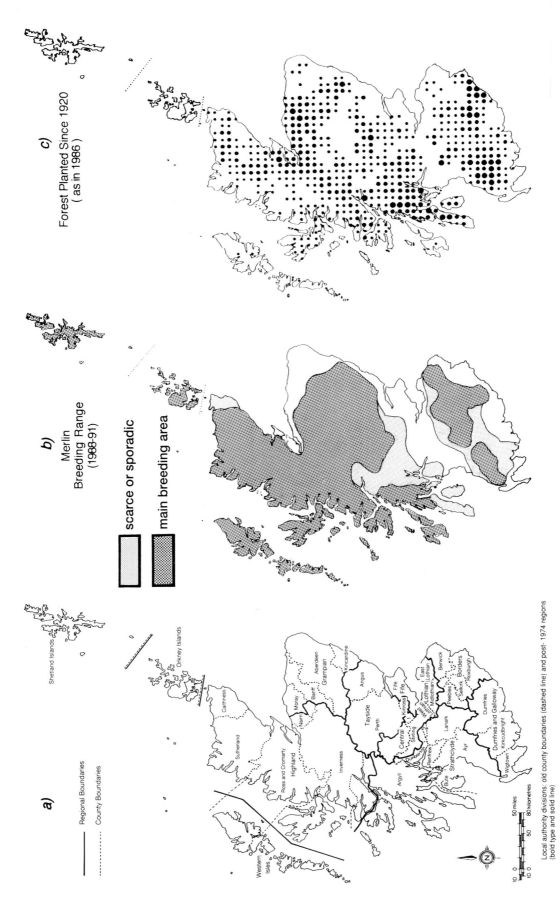

Figure 2. Maps of a) Scottish regions, b) breeding range of Scottish Merlins and c) distribution of existing forest (as in 1986) planted in every 10-km square of the National Grid since 1920. (Sources : Gibbons et al. in press; NCC 1986.)

a)

Regional Boundaries
County Boundaries

Local authority divisions: old county boundaries (dashed line) and post-1974 regions (bold type and solid line)

Shetland Islands

Orkney Islands

Western Isles

Caithness

Sutherland

Ross and Cromarty

Highland

Inverness

Argyll

Nairn

Moray

Banff

Aberdeen

Grampian

Kincardine

Angus

Tayside

Perth

Kinross

Fife

Clackmannan

Central

Stirling

Dunbarton

Renfrew

Bute

Strathclyde

Lanark

Ayr

East Lothian

Midlothian

West Lothian

Peebles

Berwick

Selkirk

Roxburgh

Borders

Dumfries

Dumfries and Galloway

Kirkcudbright

Wigtown

50 miles
80 kilometres
50
10 0
10 0

b)

Merlin
Breeding Range
(1988-91)

scarce or sporadic

main breeding area

c)

Forest Planted Since 1920
(as in 1986)

6

Table 1. Avian prey species most frequently taken by Merlins *Falco columbarius* during the breeding season in Great Britain.

Region	Merlin nesting habitat	No. of prey species taken	Total no. of prey items	Species	No. of individuals	% by no.	Source
Shetland	H	24	1245	Wheatear	491	39.4	Ellis & Okill, 1990
				Skylark	342	27.4	
				Meadow Pipit	197	15.8	
				Dunlin	64	5.1	
				House Sparrow	53	4.2	
				Rock Pipit	42	3.3	
Orkney	H	33	822	Meadow Pipit	329	40.0	Meek, 1990
				Skylark	173	21.0	
				House Sparrow	151	18.3	
				Starling	15	1.8	
				Linnet	14	1.7	
Galloway	CF	16	161	Meadow Pipit	73	45.3	Watson, 1979
				Skylark	39	24.2	
				Starling	23	14.3	
				Wheatear	7	4.3	
				Snipe	3	1.8	
Galloway	CF	15	110	Meadow Pipit	72	65.5	Orchel, 1981
				Wheatear	11	10.0	&
				Skylark	9	8.2	Table 2
	Combined :	*24*		Chaffinch	4	3.7	
Northumbria	CF,H,G	50	1917	Meadow Pipit	1117	58.3	Newton *et al.* 1984
				Skylark	237	12.3	
				Chaffinch	116	6.0	
				Starling	72	3.7	
				Wheatear	40	2.0	
Wales	CF,H,G	55	6366	Meadow Pipit	3854	60.5	Bibby, 1987
				Chaffinch	536	8.4	
				Wheatear	288	4.5	
				Whinchat	193	3.0	
				Skylark	177	2.7	
				Starling	162	2.5	
				House Sparrow	121	1.9	

(H = heather moorland nest area;
 G = grass moorland nest area;
CF = coniferous forest nest area.)

Table 2. A sample of prey taken by 4 pairs of Merlins *Falco columbarius* nesting in heather within young conifer plantations (1-20 years old) in Galloway, May-July 1977-80. (Prey remains collected by J. Orchel and identified by M. Marquiss.)

Avian prey		No. of prey items (individuals)	%
Open country species			
Meadow Pipit	*Anthus pratensis*	72	65.5
Wheatear	*Oenanth oenanthe*	11	10.0
Skylark	*Alauda arvensis*	9	8.2
Stonechat	*Saxicola torquata*	3	2.7
Pied Wagtail	*Motacilla alba*	1	0.9
Swallow	*Hirundo rustica*	1	0.9
House Martin	*Delichon urbica*	1	0.9
Sub-total		98	(89.1)
Scrub and woodland species			
Chaffinch	*Fringilla coelebs*	4	3.7
Bullfinch	*Pyrrhula pyrrhula*	2	1.8
Goldcrest	*Regulus regulus*	1	0.9
Redpoll	*Carduelis flammea*	1	0.9
Siskin	*Carduelis spinus*	1	0.9
Crossbill	*Loxia curvirostra*	1	0.9
Willow Warbler	*Phylloscopus trochilus*	1	0.9
Mistle Thrush	*Turdus viscivorus*	1	0.9
Sub-total		12	(10.9)
Total		110	(100.0)

Other prey		No.	%
Northern Eggar Moth	*Lasiocampa quercus callunae*	27	64.3
Emperor Moth	*Pavonia pavonia*	7	16.6
Fox Moth	*Macrothylacia rubi*	4	9.5
Ground beetle (sp. ?)	*Carabidae*	3	7.2
Dragonfly (sp. ?)	*Odonata*	1	2.4
Total		42	(100)

Nest of Meadow Pipit

2. 4   PREY

Wherever they occur, Merlins hunt a wide variety of avian prey, often attacking in swift low-level flight while their quarry is on or close to the ground and sometimes in prolonged aerial pursuit (Bengtson 1975, Page & Whitacre 1975, Brown 1976, Buchanan *et al.* 1988, Dekker 1988, Dickson 1988, Warkentin and Oliphant 1990). However, like many other birds of prey, Merlins tend to concentrate on those species which prove easy to capture because of their local abundance and behaviour (Trimble 1975). In Britain small, open country birds weighing less than 50 grams, such as Skylark, Meadow Pipit and Wheatear, are their preferred breeding season prey (Table 1 & 2). In some areas small woodland birds like the Chaffinch are also frequently caught, especially in the early spring when moorland prey species may not be abundant. Day-flying moths such as the Northern Eggar regularly feature in the diet and very occasionally small mammals are taken (Watson 1979, Dickson 1983, Newton *et al.* 1984, Bibby 1987, Ellis & Okill 1990).

The time when the young Merlins are being raised coincides with the nestling and fledging period of their main prey species (Coulson 1956, Cade 1982, James & Smith 1987). Whereas in Britain the young of small open-country birds are the main food source of Merlin eyasses (Armitage 1932, Roberts 1962, Bibby 1986), in Scandinavia the young of small woodland birds are often preyed upon by Merlins breeding in open birch forests (Hård & Enemar 1980, Olsson 1980) and in Iceland and Byelorussia immature waders (shorebirds) are common in their summer diet (Nielsen 1986, Dorofeyev & Ivanovski 1980).

2. 5   THE BREEDING SEASON

When the daylight hours lengthen in March and Meadow Pipits commence their northward migrations to Britain from their winter quarters in France, the Iberian Peninsula and North Africa, and migrate from Britain to northern Europe (Lack 1986, Chris Mead pers. comm.), male Merlins begin to frequent their breeding haunts in the British uplands, perching prominently on boulders, crags, stone walls, fence posts and forest tree tops to advertise their presence. Pairs are usually seen on territory from late March to early April when courtship feeding begins in earnest, accompanied by frequent chasing and calling in the chosen nesting area. Soon the female stops hunting and becomes entirely dependent on the male for food. She stays close to the nest site, driving away marauding corvids, and will not normally hunt again at any distance from the nest until the young are almost fully grown.

On bright days in spring the pair may circle above their moorland or forest nesting territory, rising higher and higher until they are merely specks in the sky. These mutual soaring displays sometimes end abruptly when the male plummets towards the earth, possibly to evict a potential rival that has strayed too close (Feldsine & Oliphant 1985, Orchel pers. obs.).

In Britain Merlins usually begin egg-laying in the first half of May. According to BTO nest record cards for the period 1937-89 the normal clutch is 4 or 5 eggs (mean = 4.16; n = 615) and the mean brood size of successful nests (n = 280) is 3.6 young, with 6 out of 10 successful pairs producing 4 or 5 fledglings (Crick *in press*). The eggs are laid at two-day intervals. Full-time incubation, which lasts 29-31 days, usually starts with the final egg. The female is responsible for most of the incubation duties, with the male sometimes covering the eggs after calling her off the nest to present food. As soon as the eggs hatch in June the frequency of prey deliveries increases. Food is generally brought by the male in the early morning hours and from late afternoon to dusk. Between 6 and 8 prey items may be provided per day to a brood of 3 large chicks (Orchel 1978).

On hatching, which usually occurs 48-50 hours after the eggs begin to pip on day 28, the tiny young weigh about 15-17 grams and are covered with a sparse white down (T I'Anson pers. comm.). Their eyes remain partly closed until the third day of life. The chicks are brooded by the female during the daytime and at night until they are 10 to 14 days old at which stage body feathers are beginning to appear beneath their thick grey down. Brooding continues through the night for some days thereafter. The growth rate of Merlin chicks is extremely rapid : at 21 days the young are already well-feathered and their wings almost fully-grown. The female eyasses can now be distinguished easily from the males by their heavier and stronger legs and feet, also by their bulkier form (Picozzi 1983, Fox 1964). Fledging generally occurs from early to mid July. Ground-nesting Merlins fledge at 26-28 days (Picozzi 1983) whereas tree-nesting young, which explore the surrounding branches, may take to the air at 29-34 days if undisturbed (Oliphant and Tessaro 1985); they are hard-penned at 38-40 days (Ruttledge 1985, T I'Anson pers. comm.). The powers of flight of newly fledged eyasses are poor. For two to four weeks after fledging they develop their flying and hunting skills but remain in or near the nesting territory dependent on the adults for much of their food. Dispersal begins in late July and early August, although there are still young at some moorland sites when grouse shooting commences on the "Glorious Twelfth" of August (B Mitchell pers. comm.).

1. Adult jack Merlin at nest in deep heather. (*Photo : Dennis Green*)

2. Merlin nesting crag in the Galloway Forest Park, 1979.

3. Hen on nest ledge.

4. Clutch of Merlin eggs.

During the 1960s and 1970s following afforestation of moorland in the Galloway Forest Park, Merlins often nested on steep slopes and vegetated crag ledges above the tree line. Productivity of nests was generally high as prey abounded in the young plantations below.

Tree nesting at the forest edge was not recorded until 1982.

5. Chicks await prey delivery.

6. Recently fledged Merlin.

7. Typical, forest-edge, nesting area of Galloway Merlins.

8. Grouse moor in the central Southern Uplands. Heather cover is maintained by light grazing and rotational burning in long narrow strips. Traditional Merlin nesting habitat.

9. Typical, moorland, foraging habitat of Galloway Merlins. Large areas of open ground separate plantations and allow Merlins to breed in this watershed.

10. Riparian corridor in an upland forest. Retention of open ground helps to maintain habitat and species diversity within forestry plantations.

11. Hen Merlin in spruce. *(Photo : Roy Blewitt)*

12. Hen feeds chicks at tree-nest in Galloway, 1986. *(Photo : Mike Callan)*

13.
Merlin chicks in a stick nest built by Hooded Crows in a Caithness plantation. Their needle-sharp talons deter small predators.

14.
Forest rangers inspect a Merlin nest in a plantation close to sea level in Caithness, July 1991. Crows start building in conifers just 3 to 4 metres high and provide nest sites for small falcons throughout the uplands.

15. Mixed-age forest in the Glenkens, south-west Scotland. Hunting habitat for ten bird of prey species in the late 1980s.

16. Short-eared Owl at nest among bracken in a young plantation. *(Photo : Mike Callan)*

17. Female approaches nesting slope. Long wings enable her to outfly small, open country birds.
(Photo : Dennis Green)

2.6   MERLINS IN WINTER

To escape the rigours of the winter months Merlins in the northern parts of their summer range migrate southward after the breeding season. For instance, birds from the boreal forests of western Canada and Alaska migrate to Central and South America; Merlins of Fenno-Scandian origin winter in Belgium and western Mediterranean countries; Icelandic birds journey to Ireland, England and France (Trimble 1975, Cade 1982, Becker & Ball 1983, Cramp & Simmons 1980, Nielsen 1986). By contrast, British Merlins are short-distance migrants. Ringing recoveries (n = 314) for the period 1911 to 1984 suggest that 70-80% of juveniles and adults winter within 100 km of their natal and breeding areas, juveniles dispersing more widely than adults. Occasional movements of 200-1700 km in a southerly direction have been recorded, particularly by birds from the Shetland Isles (Mead 1973, Heavisides 1987, Ellis & Okill 1990).

From October to February most of the upland breeding haunts of British Merlins are bleak and inhospitable. The dispersal of Merlins to lowland areas coincides with the southward movement of their main prey species in August, September and October. These months also mark the annual peak of juvenile mortality in Merlin populations (Heavisides 1987). During the winter months Merlins are widespread thoughout the British lowlands and are regularly seen on estuaries where they hunt small waders such as Dunlin and Redshank (Whitfield 1985, Lack 1986, Dickson 1988, Rebecca 1990).

The *Atlas of Wintering Birds* (Lack 1986) establishes that other potential prey species (Meadow Pipit, Skylark and Starling) are common inland on mixed and arable farmland as well as in coastal areas, with concentrations on low ground in South Scotland and southern England. Wintering Merlins observed by Dickson (1988) in south-west Scotland from 1965 to 1984 preferred to hunt small birds on farmland and "marginal" areas. Analysis of Merlin pellets found at winter roosts in eastern England and northern France (Clarke *in press*) reveals a significant overlap in breeding season and winter diets; Skylarks form a high proportion of the prey, indicating that mainly open land is hunted; this supports Dickson's findings. The continuing widespread contamination of British Merlins with toxic chemicals (DDE, PCBs, HEOD and mercury) and the shell thinning evident in several populations including Merlins breeding in the Scottish Highlands, are thought to reflect the continuing contamination of their prey species in lowland wintering areas (Newton & Haas 1988).

In south-west Scotland and England wintering Merlins have been found roosting communally (usually 2-3 birds, exceptionally 4-8 birds) in bushes and small trees at sites in lowland heath, bogs, reedbeds, washland, saltmarsh, dunes and rough grassland (Dickson 1973, Clarke 1987). In northern France, such roosts have also been found in a disused quarry overgrown with scrub and a row of poplars on farmland. All known roosting sites have ready access to open farmland and/or coastal habitat (Clarke *in press*). Judging by the marked preference of Saskatoon Merlins for roosting places in 4- to 16-metre-high conifers with substantial crown volume (Warkentin & James 1990), lowland conifer plantations may already provide ideal roosting habitat for wintering Merlins throughout the UK. It is known that Merlins roosted in a Kintyre plantation for 40 years or more; on one occasion eight birds were present in the same tree (Macintyre 1936).

Reports from landowners in Galloway indicate that dispersing and wintering Merlins frequent grassland enclaves within forestry plantations where small passerines forage (Orchel unpubl.). One observer recorded single Merlins on a 10 ha plot of rough grassland 250 m above sea level in the Galloway Forest Park on the following dates : 1986 - 27th August, 15th/16th/17th September, 3rd/17th/19th October, 2nd November, 7th December; 1987 - 7th February (J Pool pers. comm.). Studies of breeding birds trapped in Wales, Orkney and Northumberland suggest that the majority of British Merlins return to within 50 km (often within 25 km) of the natal site (Heavisides 1987). It is probable, therefore, that "local residents" are among the wintering Merlins which hunt enclaves of grazed land near forest breeding areas in south-west Scotland.

3   HISTORICAL PERSPECTIVE

3.1   MERLINS AND THE WILDWOOD OF GALLOWAY

In order to understand the present distribution of the Merlin in south-west Scotland, it is important to appreciate how natural and human-related processes have previously governed the distribution of woodland and open habitats. Fortunately, recent studies of pollen grains and macrofossils (e.g. seeds, wood and insect fragments) preserved in lake sediments and peat deposits in the Southern Uplands have enabled ecologists to reconstruct the history of plant communities, following the northward retreat of the polar ice sheets which commenced some 15,000 years ago (McVean & Ratcliffe 1962, Moar 1969, H H Birks 1972, Bishop & Coope 1977, H J Birks 1988, Jones *et al.* 1989). It is, therefore, possible today to identify those habitats with which the Merlin is likely to have been associated in the far distant past, long before the existence of written records.

From about 12,000 to 10,000 BP (before the present) the climate was cold and Galloway was largely treeless. The Gyrfalcon, Rough-legged Buzzard and Merlin probably occurred among the assemblage of birds which colonised the arctic-alpine grass-sedge tundra, heath and juniper/willow/birch scrub prevalent at the time. Locally the landscape may have resembled that of present day northern Sweden where Merlins breed in Hooded Crow nests in open birch forest and forage over nearby tundra, taking Wheatears and Meadow Pipits (Wiklund 1977, Olsson 1980). Merlin remains from this era were discovered some years ago in a Peak District cave (Jenkinson & Gilbertson 1984). At the beginning of the present Flandrian period (about 10,000 BP) the climate began to warm rapidly and by 9500 BP temperate conditions similar to those of present-day Galloway prevailed (Bishop & Coope 1977). By 9000 BP, in response to continuing climatic amelioration, the birch/hazel woodland which had become established in south-west Scotland was giving way to pine/elm/oak woodland and by 5400 BP a mixed deciduous forest, predominantly of oak/hazel/alder with some birch, elm, ash, poplar, rowan and willow, covered the Galloway landscape probably up to the summits of most hills (Birks 1972, Jones *et al.* 1989).

During this period of forest dominance (from about 9000 to 5000 BP) when the Scottish Southern Uplands were covered with dense broadleaved woodland, few Merlins probably bred in Galloway. But they would have frequented the more open pine and birch forests of northern Scotland, in whose semi-natural remnants they still nest today (Newton & Moss 1977, Knox 1990, Rebecca *et al.* 1992).

From *circa* 5400 to 2000 BP temporary forest clearances were made, first by Mesolithic hunter-gatherers, then by Neolithic, Bronze and Iron Age communities whose creation of upland pastures, coupled with the related spread of existing mires (peat bogs) from *c.* 4000 BP when the climate became more oceanic, would have re-established favourable breeding habitat for upland waders and predatory birds (Godwin 1956, Moore & Wilmott 1976, Stroud *et al.* 1987, Jones *et al.* 1989).

In early Roman times (*c.* 97 AD) when Agricola explored the coastline and forests of south-west Scotland, the Southern Uplands remained densely wooded but from about 400 AD extensive forest clearances took place, resulting in the expansion of cultivated ground, grasslands and dwarf-shrub heaths (Watt 1900, Anderson 1967, Birks 1972). There were, however, some periods of forest regeneration in the following 600 years.

After the Norman conquest, in the time of the Scottish feudal monarchs (1097-1400 AD), most of the Southern Uplands remained in the hands of the king and, where substantial areas were granted to barons and monasteries, agricultural improvement and sheep rearing flourished, often at the expense of the ancient woodland (Gilbert 1979). During this period the establishment of royal and baronial "forests" or hunting reserves in the Southern Uplands, such as the vast Forest of Buchan in Galloway (McKerlie 1878), gave a measure of protection to the remaining wildwood and its creatures. There is ample written evidence that the nesting places of falcons and hawks, required for falconry by the nobility, were strictly preserved in these "forests" (Gladstone 1910, Ritchie 1920, Anderson 1967, Carlisle 1977, Gilbert 1979). The whole of Galloway was not, however, reduced to subservience to the Scottish Crown until about 1370 AD (MacKenzie 1841, Anderson 1967).

The increasing demands made upon woodlands for timber and grazing during the period of the Stuart dynasty (1400-1603 AD) were reflected in the passage of numerous laws encouraging tree planting and increasing the penalties against "destroyers of greene wooddes and makers of mureburn" (James 5th, 4th Parliament, 1535). Towards the end of the 16th century, when Peregrines and Merlins were being flown by James 6th and Sir George Home in the hills of south-east Scotland, the timber reserves in the Lowland and Border forests were already nearing exhaustion (Muirhead 1895, Murray 1935, Carlisle 1977).

The eventual transfer of Crown lands and power to the nobility in the 17th and 18th centuries heralded a period of re-forestation by major landowners including the Dukes of Buccleuch and Earls of Galloway (Anderson 1967, Walker 1988). During the "agricultural revolution" of the 18th century, pastures in the Galloway Hills were enclosed with stone dykes (walls) and sheep and cattle management prospered; hill sheep farming continued as the major land use until the 1960s-70s when the economic balance began to tip in favour of government-aided forestry (Avery & Leslie 1990).

To summarise, man's relentless clearance of the deciduous wildwood of Galloway between 400 AD and 1650 AD was matched by a corresponding increase in the area of tilled land and semi-natural upland grasslands, bogs and heaths. The steady expansion of these habitats must have led to an increase in populations of farmland and scavenging birds as well as submontane species such as Merlin, Red Grouse and Golden Plover (Ratcliffe & Thompson 1988, Ratcliffe 1990). Communities of forest birds, however, inevitably decreased as the wildwood disappeared (Petty & Avery 1990).

3. 2 MERLINS AND GAME PRESERVATION IN SOUTH-WEST SCOTLAND : 1800 - 1945

During the nineteenth and early part of the twentieth century the Merlin benefited from heather management and an abundance of avian prey and nesting places on sporting estates in south-west Scotland. The species was widely distributed throughout moorlands in the region and the mountain ranges of the Scottish Border contained many breeding places which were "regularly returned to as those of the Peregrine" (Jardine 1834, p.131). Along with other birds of prey the Merlin was, however, systematically persecuted in the interests of game preservation. As early as 1808 the Marquis of Bute had encouraged neighbouring lairds in Argyll to employ gamekeepers suggesting they be offered "premiums" for destroying birds of prey and their nests (McWilliam 1936). Persecution of raptors was customary practice on Lord Ailsa's estates in Ayrshire some forty years later : between June 1850 and November 1854 310 "ash-coloured hawks" were destroyed by his keepers in a limited area, according to Gray & Anderson (1869).

The same authors (1869, p.8) described the Merlin as being less common in Wigtownshire than in Ayrshire where it was " in a measure restricted to moors facing the sea." Gray (1871, p.32) stated, " it cannot be called a scarce species anywhere from Caithness to Wigtownshire. Even in Ayrshire, which is overrun by keepers, it breeds in considerable numbers on the moors, especially in the north eastern quarter of the county, and appears to elude destruction by its great skill in hunting, as well as by the rapidity of its movements, when flushed from its haunts."

According to Service (1903, p.7), " In the breeding season it is rather local. It nests pretty freely on the Upper Nithsdale moors, but seems scarce and casual elsewhere in Dumfriesshire. In Galloway it is partial to moorlands near the shore during summer. During the autumn months it is a comparatively numerous species, and is then of general distribution throughout Solway."

Gladstone (1910, p.216) considered that " perhaps nowhere in Dumfriesshire is it more common than on the borders of Roxburghshire, and in upper Nithsdale where I know of one nesting place which has been annually tenanted for upwards of thirty years." Elsewhere in the county Gladstone found that the bird was subject to indiscriminate trapping and shooting so that its numbers were apparently well below the carrying capacity of the available breeding habitat : " Protected by the Wild Birds Protection Acts, with mile upon mile of ideal country for its habitat and with also almost a superabundance of small birds on which to prey, the Merlin would, if allowed, soon become once more a common resident in our uplands."

J B Hough, who made occasional forays into the Galloway Hills with the artist Jas Faed, recorded Merlins at two places near New Galloway in 1913 (Donald Watson pers. comm.) On the Wigtownshire moors Merlins bred at various sites studied from 1897-1919 by Jack G Gordon. In an unpublished study of Wigtownshire birds written in the early 1920s he stated," Today the Merlin is still not uncommon in all our moorland parishes, nesting near the same spot year after year, if undisturbed. But unfortunately most keepers indiscriminately slaughter all 'hawks' they come across, and this species suffers with the rest, although the harm it does on a grouse moor is very slight as it preys chiefly upon small birds and insects...

They seem to prefer breeding on the flat mosses and the nest is often just a scrape in a turf of heather, with perhaps a few heather 'burns' (*twigs*). Here I have never found them nesting in old nests in trees. The eggs usually number four or five, rarely six, and vary in colour from light reddish brown to dark purplish red. They are laid in early May."

In their account of Ayrshire Merlins, Paton and Pike (1929, p.106) noted that some gamekeepers had adopted an enlightened attitude towards the species : " Nests of the Merlin are to be found on many of the large moors. On some they are protected; while on others birds are shot or trapped. As an example of how the opinions of gamekeepers differ we quote the following accounts sent us by two Ayrshire men : Fairbairn, head gamekeeper at Muirkirk, says : ' *The Merlin nests on our hills in long heather, where it is very welcome. I have never, in a lifetime, seen a young Grouse at a Merlin's nest. '* Fingland, gamekeeper at Black Clauchrie, Barrhill, says : *' Two pairs of Merlins nest on our moor every year. I always destroy them if possible; they kill both Grouse and Black-Game. '* ..... Our experience of the Merlin - and it extends over a good many years - agrees with the former. We have found that on the moors of Ayrshire its staple diet consists of Meadow Pipits and Larks, though we have also noticed cock Blackbirds, Snipe and Redshank (once), and even an Emperor moth. Grouse are said to be killed by this dashing little falcon; but on only one occasion have we found a young Grouse killed *near* a Merlin's nest; and even then it was not certain how it met its death."

During the 1930s traditional grouse moor management continued throughout the South-West, including the Galloway and Carrick Hills and Wigtownshire moors, and the Merlin would have bred with mixed fortunes in many places where suitable nesting and foraging habitat prevailed. The period of the Second World War (1939-1945) marked a reprieve for the "wee blue hawk" as countrymen were called away to other duties.

3. 3 MERLIN STUDIES IN THE GALLOWAY FOREST PARK : 1946 -1985

By establishing the Glen Trool National Forest Park in Galloway in 1947 the Forestry Commission created a refuge for wildlife including all birds of prey. The Forest Park comprised five separate forests : Cairn Edward, Carrick, Changue, Glen Trool and Kirroughtree . By September 1948 the park covered 44,856 ha of which only 2,928 ha were plantation forest; it was the the Commission's intention to afforest a total of 15,279 ha leaving 29,577 ha as open land (FC 1950). By 1955 the Forest Park had expanded through acquisitions to 54,000 ha. Renamed the Galloway Forest Park in 1973, it continued to grow and today covers some 76,000 ha (760 km^2), with the bulk of the unplanted area, one third of the total, managed by the Forestry Commission as "wilderness" (Cowie 1989).

Describing bird life in the five forests of the newly designated National Forest Park, Gavin Maxwell observed that after a lapse of a few decades the Golden Eagle was " reported to be once more established in its old breeding grounds " and the Buzzard was " an abundant and typical species of the district, possibly more numerous than in any other equivalent area of the Highlands." He also noted that the Peregrine was " relatively numerous throughout Glen Trool Forest " and that the Merlin was " present in all these forests, together with the more widely distributed kestrel *Falco tinnunculus* and sparrowhawk *Accipiter nisus* " (FC 1950, p.40-41).

Derek Ratcliffe (pers. comm.) encountered Merlins at several locations in the above forests in the Galloway Hills between 1948 and 1955. However, studies at some of the Merlin nesting places in and near the Forest Park (by R C Dickson, E Langley Roberts, A Donald Watson and others) did not commence until the 1960s by which time the Galloway uplands were already the site of a major afforestation programme. Between 1951 and 1970, more than 65,000 hectares in Dumfries & Galloway Region alone were planted with conifers and a further 43,000 ha were afforested by 1980 when coniferous and broadleaved high forest covered almost 21% of the region's land area (FC 1983).

Increasing numbers of small ground-nesting birds breeding in the new conifer plantations (Moss 1979, Moss *et al*. 1979) evidently proved beneficial to the Merlin population; yet, commenting on this phenomenon in "Birds of Moor and Mountain", Donald Watson (1972, p.50) sounded a note of caution : " Fortunately, merlins are not decreasing everywhere. In and around Forestry Commission land, conditions are sometimes ideal for them. On the higher unplanted slopes, unburnt heather grows tall among bastions of grey mossy rocks. Here, on a heather-screened shelf of bare peat, the beautiful red-brown, marbled eggs are laid. Huge boulders provide essential look-out posts and prey abounds in the young trees below. But fast-maturing forests will not long remain suitable hunting grounds for merlins."

In an account written in 1971 and published in 1974, E Langley Roberts described the Merlin as " a fairly common breeding bird of the Forest Park. Its normal breeding habitat is open heathery moorland, but as more and more of this becomes covered by young plantations, it is managing to hold its own by moving up to the rocky hillsides above tree-line " (FC 1974, p.35). Indeed, one extensive area of young forest (c. 100 km^2) east of Newton Stewart held 5-6 breeding pairs in the late 1960s - early 1970s (Donald Watson pers comm). Yet, by 1979-80 only 1-2 pairs could be found (Orchel 1981, Watson 1981).

Jeff Watson (son of ADW) who studied Merlins in this area in 1973, observed that they brought prey to two ground nests (situated in deep heather at the edge of 8-year-old and 15- to 20-year-old plantations) mainly from the direction of low-lying moorland. Analysis of their prey remains revealed the Merlins' preference for small, open country passerines, in particular the Meadow Pipit, the most common breeding bird of moorland and young pre-thicket plantations. Jeff Watson (1979) concluded that "where afforestation is particularly extensive and increasing, such as in Galloway, populations of Merlins will inevitably disappear."

By the early 1980s Donald Watson considered that the predominantly ground-nesting Merlin population in its Kirkcudbrightshire stronghold near New Galloway had decreased from a peak of *circa* 15 pairs in the early 1970s to 4-5 pairs by 1978 and not more than 1 pair in 1981 (Thom 1986). It is likely, however, that in the late 1970s some pairs in the New Galloway area simply moved site and were overlooked. It is known that Merlins continued to breed successfully elsewhere in south-west Scotland : at least 6 pairs were found in Kyle & Carrick District of Strathclyde Region in 1980 (Hogg 1983). In 1982 two tree nests in tall conifers were located by the author with forest rangers (Barry Holiday and Geoff Shaw) on Forestry Commission lands in west Galloway (Orchel 1984). The nests were situated in old stick nests near the top of Sitka spruce trees planted in 1954 and 1961. This change in nest site selection had been suspected in the late 1970s by a local forester (Joe Pearce) and was probably well established in the region's forests by the early 1980s.

In 1985 concern about future management of the Merlin population on afforested lands led to the establishment of a study in Galloway conducted by the Hawk and Owl Trust in association with the Forestry Commission and a number of forest management companies. Details of the study are given below.

4   THE GALLOWAY FORESTS MERLIN PROJECT : 1986 - 1989

4. 1   SUMMARY OF RESULTS AND RECOMMENDATIONS

a) In the western Southern Uplands of Scotland in the years 1960-76 Merlins *Falco columbarius* generally nested in heather *Calluna vulgaris* on hillsides and low crags at an altitude of 100 to 400 m above sea level. The majority (n = 25 or 81%) of a sample of 31 nesting territories were located on or close to recently afforested heather and grass moorland.

b) From 1970-85 as the coniferous forests matured and more land was planted up, traditional nesting areas inside the forests were abandoned. Some moorland territories were also deserted. Of 31 nest territories occupied in the period 1960-76, by 1986-87 twenty-four (77%) had apparently been vacated.

c) Abandonment of 11 traditional nesting territories inside plantations in the years 1970-85 occurred when the trees were well-grown (at thicket stage : 3 to 10 m high) and the total area of potential moorland foraging habitat within 4 km radius (c.50 km^2) of these territories had decreased to 18.8 km^2 (37%) or less, averaging 12.7 km^2 (25%).

d) By 1986-87 ground nesting had generally been replaced by tree nesting near the edge of closed-canopy plantations, predominantly of Sitka spruce *Picea sitchensis*. Old stick nests of Carrion Crows *Corvus corone* were the preferred nest site and most Merlins nested between 200m and 400m asl. The breeding population is thought to have declined by about 30% since the late 1960s - early 1970s.

e) The majority (n = 15 or 88%) of a sample of 17 tree nests located in 1986-87 were situated close to large areas (totalling > 20 km^2 and averaging 26 km^2) of grass- and heather-dominated moorland. Fifteen (88%) of these nests were also situated within 400 m of the forest-moorland edge. Although Merlin nests were not found within 1 km of recently replanted forest plots in 1986-87, successful nesting was recorded on a 1.7 km^2 restocked plot in a major forest complex in 1989.

f) Breeding season surveys of 11 restocked pre-thicket plots showed that restructuring of coniferous forests is proving beneficial to several species of raptor and owl by providing new foraging and nesting areas. Whilst restructuring is also expected to benefit the Merlin, it is anticipated that the majority of Merlin nests in conifer plantations will continue to be located mainly in trees near forest-moorland boundaries in areas of moderate afforestation.

g) The results of this study indicate that long-term conservation of Merlin populations in the western Southern Uplands and other extensively afforested regions of Scotland will be achieved primarily by sensitive management of the remaining moorland foraging areas and nearby forest nesting habitat as well as by improvements in forest design and, where necessary, by minimising disturbance in nesting areas. The introduction of grants to promote and support increased employment of full-time wildlife managers in private sector woodlands is strongly recommended.

4.2   PROJECT AIMS

The Forestry Commission has a statutory responsibility to endeavour to achieve a reasonable balance between the production and supply of timber and the conservation of fauna of special interest (Wildlife & Countryside (Amendment) Act 1985). In keeping with this remit, in December 1985 a collaborative project was established by the Forestry Commission and the Hawk and Owl Trust to promote conservation of the Merlin on afforested lands in south-west Scotland.

In 1986 and 1987 a raptor survey was conducted on and near Forestry Commission and private forestry lands in Galloway for the following purposes:
a) to locate Merlin nesting areas;
b) to study habitat selection by Merlins;
c) to make recommendations for management of the species for inclusion in the Forestry Commission's regional wildlife conservation plans.

4.3   THE PROJECT AREA

The project area of about 3000 km^2 shown in Figure 3 lies at 55°N, 4°25'W, and covers the south-western part of the Southern Uplands of Scotland. It has been described by Birks (1972) and Marquiss *et al.* (1985) and includes the Galloway Forest Park (760 km^2) and adjacent parts of Strathclyde Region and Dumfries & Galloway Region (i.e. parts of Wigtownshire, Kirkcudbrightshire, Ayrshire and Dumfries-shire prior to local government reorganisation in 1975). The area in question is referred to as the "Galloway project area" in this report.

The underlying base-poor rocks are mainly sedimentary shales, greywackes and grits with rugged intrusions of granite south of Loch Doon (Sissons 1967). The land rises from 100 m on the flat western moors of Wigtown District to more than 790 m on the gently rounded summits of the Merrick, Rhinns Of Kells and Carsphairn Ranges of the Galloway and Carrick Hills, whose deeper valleys were carved by glaciers. Numerous rivers, including the Stinchar, Doon, Nith and Cree, noted for their runs of Atlantic Salmon, have their source in these rolling hills.

The entire region enjoys a mild, oceanic, though windy climate. Winter snow cover is brief. The mean maximum January temperature is 6.5° C and the mean maximum July temperature is 19° C (Metereological Office 1989). Rainfall is high, ranging from 120 cm/year on the western lowlands to 170 cm in the hills at 300 m and exceeding 250 cm on the high tops. Over large parts of the region organic soils predominate : peats, peaty rankers, peaty podzols and gleys - land classes 5 and 6 suited only to improved grassland and rough grazings (Birse & Robertson 1976, Brown *et al.* 1982).

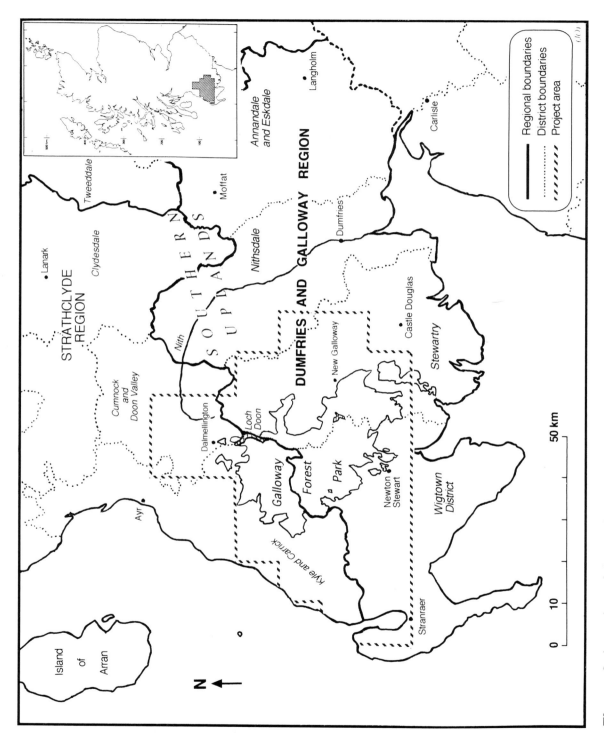

Figure 3. Location of the project area in south-west Scotland.

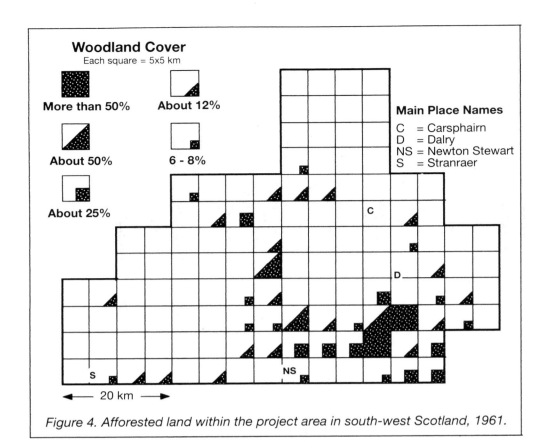

Figure 4. Afforested land within the project area in south-west Scotland, 1961.

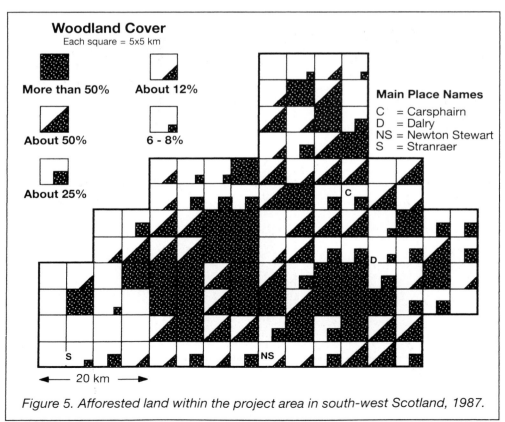

Figure 5. Afforested land within the project area in south-west Scotland, 1987.

Forestry, hill sheep and cattle farming are the major land uses. Extensive plantations of spruce, larch and pine cover many hillsides below 400 m and are home to Scotland's finest Red Deer (Davies 1987, Ratcliffe 1987). Whilst many forests are now in second rotation, in some districts newly afforested ground is widespread.

Areas of semi-natural acidic grassy moorland and moist Atlantic heather moor have become greatly fragmented by afforestation (Figure 4 & 5). The sheep-walks are dominated by bents, sheep's fescue, wavy hair-grass and sweet vernal-grass, frequently invaded by bracken on drier soils and mat-grass, flying bent (purple moor-grass) and heath rush on wetter ground. The characteristic vegetation of the remaining heather-dominated moorlands comprises heathers *Calluna / Erica* spp., cotton-grass, deer- grass, flying bent and bog-mosses with patches of bog myrtle in wet areas and bilberry on drier ground (Matthews 1974, McVean and Ratcliffe 1962, Ratcliffe 1977, Denise Reed pers. comm.). Moorland management for Red Grouse which was widely practised in the 1920s-30s and continued on some of the western moors until the early 1970s is no longer of sporting or economic significance though there has recently been a revival of local interest (D Anderson pers. comm.).

4. 4   THE GALLOWAY FORESTS MERLIN SURVEY : 1986 - 1987

4. 4. 1   THE OBSERVERS
Data were gathered for the Galloway Forests Merlin Survey (1986-87) by the following observers : Forestry Commission rangers in Ayrshire & Arran Forest District, Newton Stewart FD and Castle Douglas FD; wildlife managers and foresters active on private forestry lands (managed by Economic Forestry Group, Fountain Forestry, Lambert Jackson, Scottish Woodlands and Tilhill Forestry); gamekeepers, local ornithologists and the project co-ordinators, Jack Orchel (Hawk & Owl Trust) and John Livingstone (Forestry Commission).

4. 4. 2   STUDY AREAS AND METHODS
Before the survey began information about traditional and recently occupied Merlin nesting areas was pooled by the project co-ordinators and additional nesting area data were obtained via a retrospective questionnaire circulated to all survey participants and others with specialist knowledge of the region. In the interests of the Merlin nests it was agreed by the coordinators that breeding birds and their dependent young should not be disturbed intentionally at or near the nest by any of the survey workers. Traditional nesting areas and 22 of the occupied Merlin territories located in 1986-87 were, however, visited under licence by the author to confirm the presence of breeding birds. Follow-up studies in parts of the project area (as well as in several north and south-east Scotland forests) were conducted by JO from 1988 to 1991.

A number of study areas (mean size 8.5 km^2) were selected for close study by the team of 25 observers in 1986 and the 44 observers in 1987 (Table 3). Much of the grass-dominated "moorland and mountain" ground in the project area (Table 4) lacked suitable ground vegetation for nesting cover and had no history of occupation by Merlins. All the study areas were, therefore, selected on the basis that they contained known or potential nesting places in rank heather and/or in thicket, pole stage and older conifers as well as abundant foraging habitat nearby i.e. heather and grass moorland and recently afforested and/or restocked ground.

Coverage increased during the survey period : 25 study areas were surveyed in 1986 and 55 in 1987. The total area chosen for close study increased from 214 km^2 (1986) to 462 km^2 (1987) ; in 1987 this represented about 40% of the afforested land and about 7% of the "moorland and mountain " ground in the project area. Figure 6 shows the distribution of study areas per 10-km square within the project area. The habitat features of the study areas and details of their distribution according to forest district are presented in Table 5.

Forestry Commission and private forestry company employees were asked to record survey data as part of their normal duties. In the case of forest rangers and stalkers this involved dawn and evening visits to pre-thicket plantations, forest edges and glades. Every observer used a standardised mapping method specifically devised for the project : this required multiple visits to a given study area or areas from the beginning of April through July to record sightings of all raptors, owls, corvids and Cuckoos, on species checklists and large-scale maps (1: 25,000). These were assembled in survey logbooks containing full survey instructions (Appendix 6) and a bird identification chart. To aid species recognition, a copy of "The Birdwatcher's Pocket Guide" (Hayman 1985) was issued to each observer.

In order to help identify active Merlin nesting areas and nest sites the survey workers were also asked to record every Merlin sighting not only within but also outside their study areas and to make a note of Merlin behaviour. Sightings of corvids (Ravens , Carrion Crows and Magpies) were also noted because these birds provide nests for falcons and are sometimes attacked by territory-holding Merlins. Cuckoos, which are similar in shape and size to the Merlin, were recorded to help draw the observers' attention to the fact that they should not be confused with this much rarer falcon. Most observers managed to map and chart data in their study areas on more than six occasions in each annual survey period. Typical survey records are shown in Appendix 7 & 8.

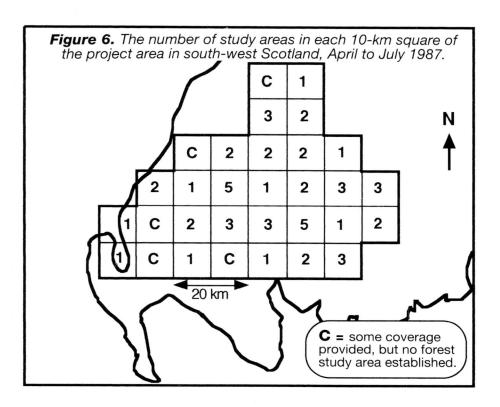

Figure 6. The number of study areas in each 10-km square of the project area in south-west Scotland, April to July 1987.

C = some coverage provided, but no forest study area established.

Table 3. Distribution of study areas (by size) in the Galloway project area, 1987.

Size of study area (km^2)	0.2 - 2	3-4	5-8	9-12	13-16	Sub-total	
No. of study areas	6	10	20	10	4	50	
Size of study area (km^2)	17-20	21-24	25-28	29-32	33-36	Sub-total	**Total**
No. of study areas	1	1	0	1	2	5	**55**

Table 4. Main habitats within the project area in south-west Scotland, 1987.

Habitat	(A) Project area		(B) 55 study areas		B as % of A
	km^2	%	km^2	%	%
Woodland *	1037	33	395	13	38
Moorland & mountain	1012	33	63	2	7
Enclosed farmland	775	25	4	< 0.2	0.5
Other (water etc.)	276	9	-	-	-
Total	3100	(100)	**462**	(15)	

* Mainly mixed-age coniferous forest

Table 5. Main habitats in the 55 forest study areas in south-west Scotland, 1987.

	Forest Districts							
	Newton Stewart		Ayrshire & Arran		Castle Douglas		All districts	
No. of study areas	(19)		(10)		(26)		(55)	
	Area km²	%	Area km²	%	Area km²	%	Area km²	%
Main habitats								
Mountain & moorland	22	14	23	16	22	14	67	14
High forest planted 1930-79*	72	45	101	69	99	63	272	59
Young forest planted 1980-87	57	36	20	14	29	18	106	23
Forest replanted 1980-87	8	5	1	< 1	8	5	17	4
Total area	**159**		**145**		**158**		**462**	(100)

(* Mainly coniferous woodland planted after 1950.)

At the end of each breeding season a summary chart was prepared to show presence/absence data and breeding evidence for the target species in each study area. Those who had reported Merlins in and near study areas not monitored by JO and JL were visited to check the accuracy of data provided. Where there was any doubt concerning Merlin identification the relevant record was deleted from the final analysis. By scrutinising all the survey notes, maps and checklists and on the basis of these discussions with observers, it was possible to identify areas where Merlins had definitely, probably and possibly bred, following the British Trust for Ornithology survey criteria (Sharrock 1976, p.17). Breeding was considered "confirmed" (definite) if the following evidence was recorded by the observers and/or the project coordinators : a nest containing young ; recently fledged young at or near the nest; a male or female repeatedly carrying prey to a nest site from which food begging calls were heard. "Probable breeding" was recorded if a pair was seen engaging in breeding behaviour such as a food transfer or if a single bird or pair was holding territory (as demonstrated by hen Merlin alarm calls indicating the presence of a nest containing young or an adult/adults aggressively driving away an avian predator). "Possible breeding" refers to a single bird (blue-grey male / brown female / brown immature) seen in suitable nesting habitat more than 5 km from the nearest occupied nest territory during the breeding season.

In order to avoid unnecessary disturbance, nest trees (except that shown in Photo 12) were not climbed. Previous nest inspections and frequent sightings of Carrion Crows recorded in Merlin nesting areas, had already established that the majority of Merlins were breeding in abandoned Carrion Crow nests.

Vegetation was mapped for a circle of 4 km radius, "believed to encompass most of the range which breeding Merlins hunted" (Bibby 1986) for each of a sample of 20 nest sites found in 1986-87 and for an additional 2 sites located during follow-up studies in 1988-91. Ten categories were mapped. These were heather-dominated moorland, grass moorland (i.e.unimproved grassland), improved grassland, arable land, first and second rotation pre-thicket conifer plantations (1-7 years old), well-grown conifer forest (8 to 50+ years old), broadleaved woodland and scrub. Forest habitat data were derived from forestry stock maps (scale 1:10,560). Details of the other vegetation types were obtained from field surveys conducted by the author in autumn and springtime of the immediate post-survey period. Ordnance Survey maps (scale 1: 25,000) were used to calculate the area of unplanted moorland and farmland habitats outside the forest boundary. The length of mature forest edge and forest roads was likewise derived from large-scale OS maps and stock maps as was the area of built land and water (lochs, rivers etc.). Field surveys yielded the limited hedgerow and scrub data, both habitats being scarce in the project area. The area of unafforested moorland remaining in 1987 within 4 km radius of a sample of eleven abandoned Merlin territories was also calculated using large-scale OS maps.

5   RESULTS

In this study the data are assembled into three survey periods : 1960-76 (data provided by A D Watson and others); 1977-85 (data gathered by JO and others); 1986-87 (data from the Galloway Forests Merlin Survey). Reference is also made to four nests found between 1988 and 1991. Data from 1946-59 are not shown as most of the nesting areas reported then were still active and hence the same as those found in the 1960s.

5. 1   HISTORICAL INFORMATION : 1946 - 1985

On managed heather moorland Merlins are known to occupy traditional nesting areas or nesting territories where the location of the actual nest (the nest site) may vary slightly from year to year (Rowan 1921-2). The nesting area lies within a large home range which contains the roosting and foraging areas of the pair. The home ranges of neighbouring pairs may sometimes overlap but the vicinity of the nest site is defended against conspecifics and large avian predators (Newton *et al.* 1978). In general the distance between nesting pairs is not less than 1.5 km and is usually greater than 3 km but in exceptional circumstances e.g. where topography allows and prey is abundant, pairs may nest less than 1 km apart (Roberts & Green 1983). In plantation forest the same general area may attract tree-nesting Merlins in different years and mean nearest-neighbour distances may be 4 to 6 km where there is continuity of nesting and foraging habitat (see Section 5.2; also Parr 1991). Normally only 40-60% of nesting territories are occupied in any year (Bibby 1986, Nielsen 1986, Rebecca 1989, Parr 1991). In this study the nesting area or territory is defined as an area of 1 km radius around a nest site or several alternative sites used in different years.

The retrospective questionnaire issued to members of the survey team, plus other enquiries, yielded information about 15 nesting areas used in 1946-59 and more than 60 nesting territories deemed to have been occupied by Merlins for one or more seasons in the period 1960-85. Owing to lack of firm breeding evidence such as eggs, young or adults carrying prey to a nest, many of the retrospective records could not be included in the comparative analyses presented below (Section 5). Nevertheless, the retrospective study proved important as it clearly established that birds had bred on one or more occasion in 31 territories from 1960-76 and in 25 territories in the years 1977-85. In the latter period (1977-85) pairs still nested within 3 km of 17 (55%) territories occupied in the years 1960-76; however, in 1986-87 birds were found breeding or holding territory within 3 km of only 7 (23%) of the 1960-76 nesting areas.

Evidence from the best studied district of 700 km^2 suggests that a population of 7-8 pairs (1.1 pairs/100 km^2) in the early 1960s had increased to 12-13 pairs (1.8 pairs/100 km^2) by the late 1960s - early 1970s when Merlins were nesting in and close to young plantations in which open country prey was abundant and vulnerable; this increase may, however, simply reflect improved local coverage during the *Atlas* period (1968-72). Some 15 years later, between 1986 and 1989, no more than 6 breeding pairs (0.8 pairs/100 km^2) were found in the same area in a single year (Figure 7).

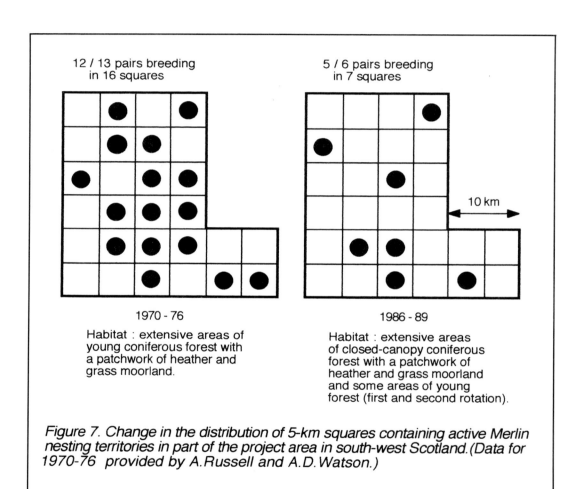

12 / 13 pairs breeding in 16 squares

5 / 6 pairs breeding in 7 squares

10 km

1970 - 76

Habitat : extensive areas of young coniferous forest with a patchwork of heather and grass moorland.

1986 - 89

Habitat : extensive areas of closed-canopy coniferous forest with a patchwork of heather and grass moorland and some areas of young forest (first and second rotation).

Figure 7. Change in the distribution of 5-km squares containing active Merlin nesting territories in part of the project area in south-west Scotland.(Data for 1970-76 provided by A.Russell and A.D.Watson.)

The abundance of prey in young plantations during the 1960s and early 1970s would have permitted some birds to lay early clutches as noted by Dickson & Watson (1974) and frequently allowed ground-nesting pairs in and near young conifer forests to rear large broods (mean brood size : 4.2 young [n=24]). However, not all ground nests were successful as a sample of breeding records shows (Table 6).

Table 6. Breeding success of Merlins at a sample of ground nests (n = 37) in and near young conifer forests in Galloway, 1960-81. (Data for 1960-76 provided by A. D. Watson.)

Breeding outcome	Nests	
	No.	%
Successful nests		
Nest with eggs & large young	24	64.9
Failed nests		
Nest site burnt out	1	2.7
Eggs disappeared (stolen?)	4	10.8
Eggs did not hatch	2	5.4
Eggs broken into large fragments	1	2.7
Nesting female killed by predator	1	2.7
Brood killed by predator	4	10.8
Total	37	(100)

The years 1970-85 were characterised by abandonment of nesting areas within and near young plantations where pairs nested typically in rank heather on hillsides or occasionally on vegetated crag ledges. At least 18 territories were vacated in the project area, 8 of which had a history of fairly regular use for more than 10 years. Afforestation of heather and grass moorland which fragmented and eventually reduced the size of moorland foraging areas and obliterated nesting places is thought to have accounted for the loss of 11 territories. In addition, 3 widely spaced nesting areas in rank heather on former grouse moors were destroyed by large-scale muirburning intended to improve sheep pasture. Regular hill-walking in the pre-laying period probably made 2 other nesting areas untenable. Two apparently suitable heather moorland nesting areas near young plantations were also vacated for unknown reasons (Table 7). Pairs may have moved some distance to avoid ground predators or to nest in conifers as occurred in one South Ayrshire forest complex in 1982/3.

Table 7. Factors considered to be responsible for abandonment of a sample of Merlin nesting territories (n = 18) in south-west Scotland, 1970-85. (Nesting territory = an area of 1 km radius (3.1 km^2) around a nest site or group of alternative sites occupied in different years.).

Probable cause of territory loss (1970-85)	No. of territories	%
1. Afforestation of foraging areas	9	50.0
2. Afforestation of nest sites	2	11.1
3. Destruction of moorland nest areas by fire	3	16.7
4. Disturbance of forest nest areas by hill walkers	2	11.1
5. Unknown	2	11.1
Total	18	(100)

There is some evidence to suggest that the local Peregrine population, which increased dramatically in the period 1974-82 (Mearns and Newton 1988), may have excluded Merlins from some traditional and potential nesting places on secondary crags and steep heathery slopes (within and outside plantations) and therefore hastened their occupation of new tree sites at the forest edge. In 1979 Dick Roxburgh (pers. comm.) witnessed an aerial conflict above a forest crag site regularly occupied by Merlins : " The wardening at Loch... provided many sightings of the Merlin near its original stronghold. I did see twice a Peregrine attacking this Merlin, once a very spectacular stoop and both crashing among the trees. I did not see the result but the Peregrine was soon to move on. I wondered at the time if this was within the hunting territory of the Peregrine but there is no known site really near enough."

The Merlin in question was found dead by the author in late June, ten metres from her nest which contained three unhatched eggs from an original clutch of five. She was in her sixth calendar year and had been ringed as an eyass 110 km ENE (Newton *et al.* 1986). The bird would undoubtedly have been defending her nesting territory when Roxburgh noticed the aerial combat. Today the site is occupied by Peregrines!

The above example of inter-specific conflict must, however, be set in a broader context. During the 1970s and 1980s there was apparently no lack of alternative nesting sites for Merlins, either in trees or in deep heather, throughout the project area. A number of pairs bred successfully within 2 km of Peregrine nest sites. The mean distance between 5 regularly used Merlin nesting areas and nearby Peregrine nesting crags was 1.85 km (range : 0.75 to 3 km). Only 3 traditional Merlin nest territories were permanently occupied by Peregrines in the mid 1980s and this occurred some time after canopy closure in the surrounding plantations had eliminated important foraging areas, probably already rendering the nesting places unattractive to breeding Merlins.

Notwithstanding the various factors described above, some of which may have contributed to occupation and others to abandonment of particular nesting territories in the project area, some Galloway Merlins evidently managed to adapt to rapidly changing circumstances as the 1986-87 survey was to reveal.

5. 2   MERLIN SURVEY SUMMARY : 1986 -1987

Seventeen occupied Merlin territories were located in the project area in 1986 and 19 in 1987. Breeding was confirmed or considered probable in 14 territories during 1986 and 15 in 1987, making a total of 29 such territories for both years of the survey. As only 5 of these nesting territories were occupied by breeding pairs in both years, the actual number of discrete nesting territories where breeding was confirmed or considered probable in 1986-87 totalled 24. For the same reason, the total number of separate nesting territories where breeding was considered possible, probable and confirmed in 1986-87 proved to be 31 (Table 8). The mean nearest neighbour distance of 10 pairs which nested in conifers in 1987 was 5.1 km (range 3.2 to 8.4 km), the majority of pairs nesting 4 to 5.5 km apart.

The survey data were mapped on the 10-km squares of the National Grid and compared with the 1968-72 Merlin data from the *Atlas of Breeding Birds* (Sharrock 1976) in order to show possible changes in distribution and abundance of the species over the past two decades (Figures 8 & 9). This comparison revealed that the Merlin had continued to breed throughout the more recently afforested northern and western parts of the project area but was not found in 1986-87 as a confirmed or probable breeder in parts of its former stronghold in the south-east, one of the most densely afforested areas in the British Isles.

Whilst a simple statistical comparison of the *Atlas* and 1986-87 breeding data (Table 9) might at first glance suggest no overall decline in the region's Merlin population, it is important to note the following points : 1) the *Atlas* symbols do not indicate whether one or more pairs nested in a given 10-km square and can only be used as a measure of the species' distribution; 2) more thorough coverage of potential breeding areas in the 1986-87 study in some of the western and north-western squares may have revealed territories which were active though undetected in the earlier *Atlas* period; 3) Merlin numbers may recently have increased in the western and north-western squares (possibly in response to newly afforested moorland providing increased availability of preferred prey close to nesting places in high coniferous forest) thereby compensating for a decrease in Merlin numbers in the south-east.

Table 8. The number of Merlin territories located during the Galloway Forests Merlin Survey of 1986-87.

Territory	1986 No.	1987 No.	1986 & 87 No.	
Where breeding confirmed *	13	12	25	(a)
Where breeding probable **	1	3	4	
Where breeding possible ***	3	4	7	
Total	17	19	36	(b)

*	Evidence of **confirmed breeding** = young in nest (2 territories); fledged young being fed by adult at or close to nest (7 territories); adult bird/s repeatedly carrying prey to nest (16 territories).
**	Evidence of **probable breeding** = pair attacking avian predator (2 territories); courtship feeding (2 territories);
***	Evidence of **possible breeding** = single bird seen on one or more occasions in suitable breeding habitat > 5 km from nearest pair (7 territories).
	(a) Actual total = 20 discrete territories where breeding was confirmed since 5 territories were occupied in both years.
	(b) Actual total = 31 territories for reason stated in a).

Table 9. The number of 10-km squares in which Merlins were recorded during the breeding season in the Galloway project area in 1968-72 (*Atlas of Breeding Birds* data) and in 1986-87.

| Survey period | Breeding | | | | | Not | |
	Conf.	Prob.	Poss.	No.	%	recorded	%
1968-72	7	7	8	22	71	9	29
1986-87	14	4	4	22	71	9	29

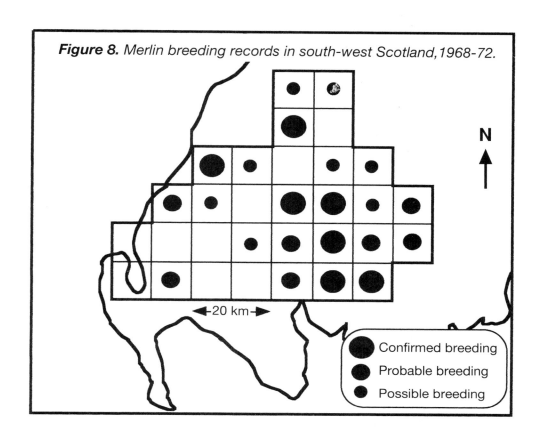

Figure 8. Merlin breeding records in south-west Scotland, 1968-72.

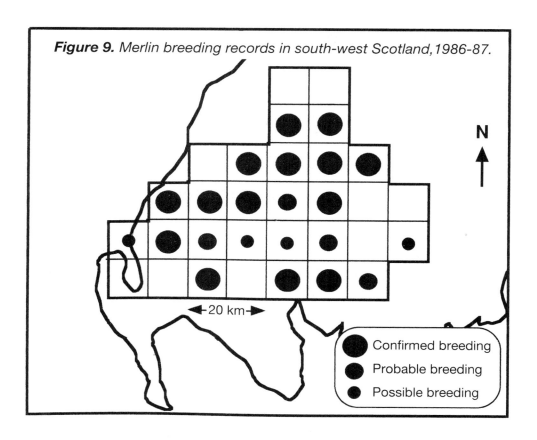

Figure 9. Merlin breeding records in south-west Scotland, 1986-87.

5.3 NEST SITE SELECTION : 1960 - 1987

Although there appeared to be no shortage of suitable nesting places on heather-covered hillsides within and above mixed-age conifer plantations, in 1986-87 the majority (n = 17) of a sample of 20 pairs preferred to breed in abandoned stick nests, 16 of which were situated in thicket stage and older coniferous forest. Only 3 pairs nested in rank heather on open moorland, a marked change from the 1960s and 1970s when nesting in heather on hillsides and low crags was the norm (Figure 10). It is important to note that these survey results may under-represent the size of the moorland-nesting population as much of the remaining unplanted ground in the project area was not subject to systematic searches (see Table 4 & Figure 6). However, most of this ground was considered unsuitable as nesting habitat for Merlins.

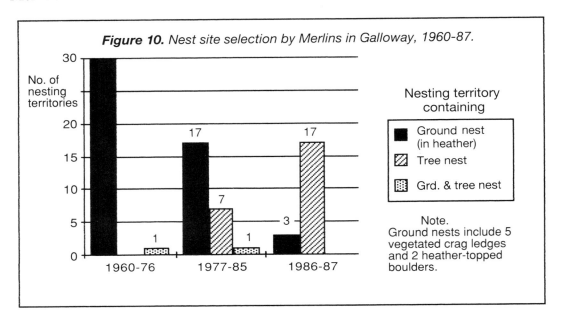

Figure 10. Nest site selection by Merlins in Galloway, 1960-87.

Three nests were located in compartments of Sitka spruce, 12 in compartments of Sitka spruce mixed with Lodgepole pine and/or larch, and one nest was found in a small block of Norway spruce on heather moorland close to a well-grown and extensive forest. The age of nest trees varied considerably (Table 10), the youngest being a Sitka spruce (height c. 4.5 m) in a 13-year-old plantation and the oldest also a Sitka (c.12 m) growing in a 32-year-old plantation. Three of these pairs selected sites in a narrow (150-600 m) belt of woodland several kilometres in length. The majority of the nests utilised by Merlins were situated high in the forest canopy in unthinned stands on gently sloping ground. Tall trees in the vicinity of the nest tree provided perches with a good view of the surrounding area. One pair bred successfully in an old Carrion Crow nest built in a Hawthorn tree adjacent to a plantation of pre-thicket and thicket-stage trees.

Table 10. Age of conifer plantations used by tree-nesting Merlins in Galloway, 1986-87. (Note. Trees are normally planted when 3 years old.)

Age of compartment (yrs)	1-10	11-15	16-20	21-25	26-30	31-35	Total
Number of nests	0	3	5	5	1	2	16
%	0	19	31	31	6	13	(100)

The discovery in 1991 of the tree nest shown in Photos 13 and 14, approximately 2.5 m off the ground in a Lodgepople pine (height c. 4.25 m) situated 120 m from the edge of a 10-year-old plantation, indicates that old corvid nests are available and readily utilised by Merlins early in the forest cycle, thus confirming the 1980-83 findings of Newton *et al.* (1986a) and those of Little and Davison (1992) in northern England.

In 1989 a pair of Merlins nested and reared three young on a 170 ha restocked site east of the Galloway project area. The nest was in a patch of rank heather among a crop of young Lodgepole pine and Sitka spruce. A pair of Hen Harriers bred successfully on the same plot in 1990. Further details about the nesting area and surrounding habitats are given below in Section 5.12.

5.4   ALTITUDE OF NESTS : 1960 - 1987

The altitudes of 20 nest sites found in 1986-87 ranged from 170 m to 450 m above sea level. The majority (n = 18) were located between 200 m and 400 m. In the years 1960-87 seventy per cent of nests were situated at this altitude. Table 7 shows that from 1960 to 1987 there was a decline in the number of sites occupied below 200 m but no evidence of a corresponding decline at less afforested, higher altitudes.

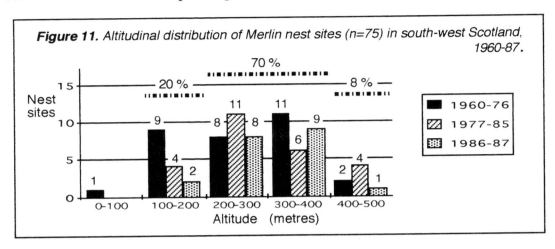

Figure 11. Altitudinal distribution of Merlin nest sites (n=75) in south-west Scotland, 1960-87.

5.5   ACCESS TO MOORLAND FORAGING AREAS : 1986 - 1987

Access to open ground and moorland foraging areas would appear to be important to forest-nesting Merlins. Fifteen (88%) of 17 tree-nests were situated within 400 m of the nearest forest-moorland boundary (mean distance to moorland = 167 m); five of these were located within 50 m of the forest edge. Two other nests in stands of mature conifers were found more than 1 km from the forest edge but within 50 m of very young plantations established on heather moor. The majority (n = 15 or 88%) of 17 tree nests were also situated close to forest glades i.e. rides, roads and unplanted streamsides, which provided access to the nest site and in which food passes frequently took place.

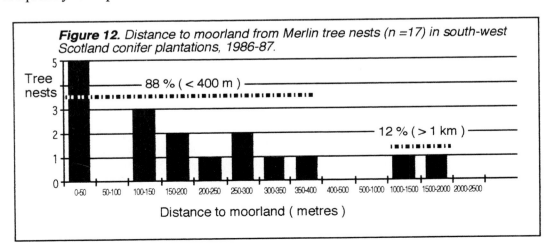

Figure 12. Distance to moorland from Merlin tree nests (n =17) in south-west Scotland conifer plantations, 1986-87.

5.6   NESTING AREAS : 1960 - 1987

Analysis of the major habitat components within 1 km radius of 20 nests located in 1986-87 showed that 18 (90%) pairs selected nest sites with substantial areas of heather and/or grass moorland nearby. Nine (45%) nesting areas comprised two vegetation types : high forest and moorland. Merlin nests were not found deep within extensive, unbroken, closed-canopy plantations. Table 11 shows that the association of Merlin nests with heather and grass moorland was also an important feature of at least 90% of nesting areas occupied from 1960 to 1985. By contrast, in the period 1960-87 the number and percentage of nest sites found on or adjacent to recently afforested hill ground decreased steadily from 25 (81%) of a sample of 31 in 1960-76 to 9 (45%) of a sample of 20 nests in 1986-87, reflecting the steady disappearance of this ephemeral prey-rich habitat and the increased availability of nesting places in well-grown forest adjacent to open hill ground.

Table 11. Main habitats within 1 km radius of Merlin nest sites in Galloway, 1960 - 87. (Habitat categories C and F do not include restocked sites.)

Habitat categories	1960-76 No. of sites	%	1977-85 No. of sites	%	1986-87 No. of sites	%
A. Moorland	6	19.3	5	20	2	10
B. Young forest / moorland	20	64.5	6	24	1	5
C. Mixed-age forest / moorland	2	6.5	10	40	6	30
D. Well-grown forest / moorland	0	0	4	16	9	45
E Young forest (1-7 yrs)	2	6.5	0	0	0	0
F. Mixed-age forest	1	3.2	0	0	2	10
G. Well-grown forest (8-50+ yrs)	0	0	0	0	0	0
Total	31	(100)	25	(100)	20	(100)
Total nest sites associated with recently afforested ground	25	(81)	16	(64)	9	(45)
Total nest sites associated with grass and heather moorland	28	(90)	25	(100)	18	(90)

Like the North American race *Falco c. richardsonii* breeding in old corvid (Magpie) nests in coniferous forest overlooking open prairie/grasslands in south-eastern Montana (Sieg & Becker 1990), during the 1980s most Galloway Merlins bred in old corvid (Carrion Crow) nests in coniferous woodland which combined easy access to the nest site and open country foraging areas with maximum concealment of the nest contents.

5. 7   MOORLAND FORAGING AREAS : 1986 -1987

In Britain from late April through July both forest-nesting and moorland-nesting Merlins prey heavily on small moorland birds (Watson 1979, Newton *et al.* 1984, Bibby 1987, Parr *in press*). As these ground-nesting species are usually present at fairly low densities on heather and grass moorland (Moss 1979, Seel & Walton 1979, Watson & O'Hare 1979, Currie 1981) and since more than 85% of hunting flights at small passerines may be unsuccessful (Rudebeck 1951, Dekker 1988), male Merlins must forage widely over open country. Brown (1976) estimated that each male needs to catch some 450 small birds to feed himself, his mate and typical brood of 3 young during the breeding season i.e. from courtship to when the fledged young disperse . A total of 730-800 sparrow-sized birds could be the prey requirements of a breeding pair of Richardson's Merlins and their 4 young over a 120-day breeding season according to Oliphant & Tessaro (1985).

In order to obtain an idea of the amount of moorland required to support one pair of European Merlins and their normal brood of 3-4 young, the area of potential, unafforested, foraging habitat (semi-natural grassland, improved grassland and heather moor) within 4 km radius (50.2 km^2) of a sample of 20 nesting territories occupied by breeding birds in 1986-87 was measured. As stated previously in Section 4.4.2, the radius of 4 km was selected because it was considered to encompass most of the range hunted by breeding Merlins, according to studies of their hunting behaviour and prey in Wales (Bibby 1986, 1987), validated by a study of prey remains found near Merlin nest sites in south-east Grampian Region in 1984-1988 (Rebecca *et al.* 1990).

Analysis of these habitat data revealed that **18 (90%) of 20 Galloway pairs had access to more than 20 km^2 (2000 ha) of unafforested hill ground within 4 km of the nest.** This group included all 9 pairs breeding in high forest - moorland nesting territories. **The mean area of grass and heather moorland within 4 km radius of 17 forest nesting territories and of 3 moorland nesting areas was 26 km^2 and 35.6 km^2 respectively** (Figure 13 & 14, Table 13, Appendix 2). **By contrast, in 1987 the area of unafforested hill ground remaining within 4 km of 11 nesting territories which had been abandoned in the pre-survey period (1970-85) was less extensive and averaged 12.7 km^2** (SD 4.26, range 5.66 - 18.8).

The mean area of moorland per occupied territory (27.4 km^2, SD 7.94, range 6.9 - 35.9, n = 20; one-tailed *t*-test *t* = 5.662, P < 0.001) **and per occupied, high forest nesting territory (26.02 km^2,** SD 7.67, range 6.9 - 33.3, n = 17; one-tailed *t*-test *t* = 5.191, P < 0.001) **was, therefore, found to be significantly higher than the mean moorland area per territory abandoned in the initial, thicket stage of the forest cycle.**

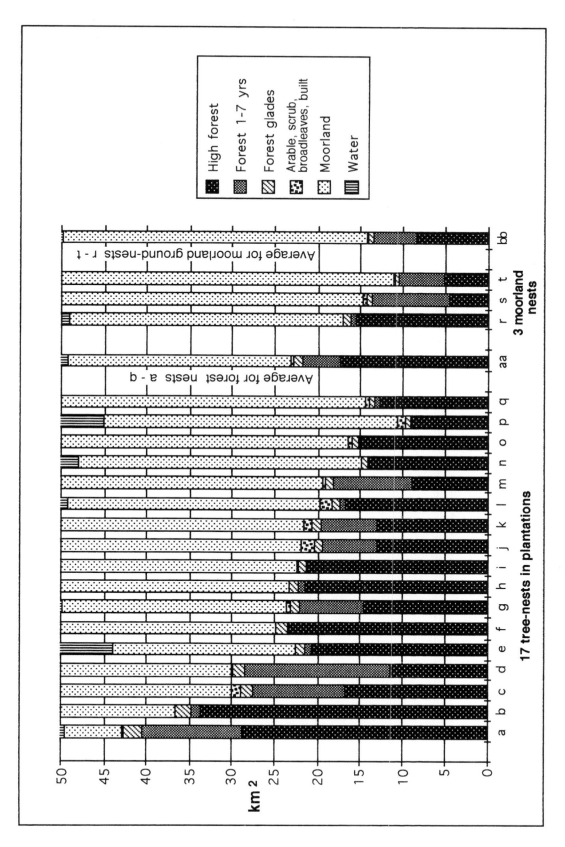

Figure 13. *The main habitats within 4 km radius (c. 50 km2) of a sample of Merlin nests (n=20) in the western Southern Uplands of Scotland, 1986-87.*

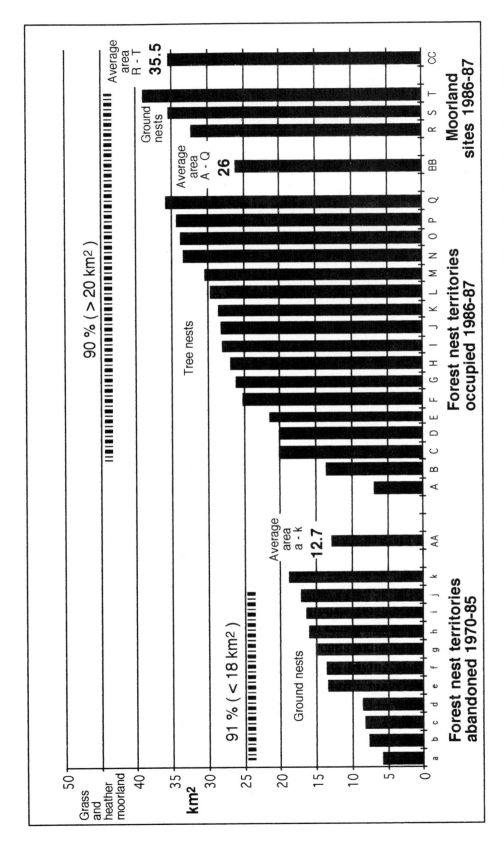

Figure 14. *Moorland foraging habitat available in 1987 within 4 km radius (c.50 km²) of abandoned (n = 11) and active (n = 20) Merlin nest territories on afforested lands in the western Southern Uplands of Scotland.*

52

Table 12. The area of grass and heather moorland remaining in 1987 within 4 km radius (c. 50 km^2) of a sample of Merlin nesting territories occupied in 1986-87 (n =17) and territories abandoned in 1970-85 (n = 11) on afforested lands in south-west Scotland,

Grass and heather moorland *	Forest territories occupied 1986-87			Forest territories abandoned 1970-85		
km^2	No.		%	No.		%
1-4	-			-		
4-6	-			1		
6-8	1**			1	4	(36)
8-10	-	2	(12)	2		
10-12	-			-		
12-14	1***			2		
14-16	-			2	7	(64)
16-18	-			2		
18-20	-			1****		
20-22	3			-		
22-24	-			-		
24-26	1			-		
26-28	3			-		
28-30	3	15	(88)	-	0	
30-32	1			-		
32-34	2			-		
34-36	2			-		
Total	**17**		(100)	**11**		(100)

*   Figures shown include improved grassland (column **d** in Appendix 2).
**   Nest 4 in Table 13 & Appendix 2, close to new prey-rich, pre-thicket plantations.
***   Nest 7 in Table 13 & Appendix 2, 420 m asl ; extensive grass moorland foraging habitat available just beyond 4 km range.
****   Moorland foraging areas (within 4 km radius of former Merlin nesting area) which contain 3 active Peregrine nest territories.

The Galloway habitat data presented in this report (Figure13 & 14, Table 12 & 13, Appendix 2) suggest that **the minimum area of grass and heather moorland required to support a pair of breeding Merlins is about 20 km^2**. It must be borne in mind, however, that the moorland soils in west Galloway are predominantly poor quality acidic peats on base-poor rocks; therefore, at higher altitudes (350-500 m asl) where open country prey species tend to be less abundant (Rose 1982), Merlin home ranges may be considerably larger. In order to provision their mates and offspring at higher altitudes, male Merlins may often need to hunt futher than 4 km from the nest. The converse may well apply in prey-rich areas such as keepered grouse moors where relatively high Merlin densities have been recorded.

Tracking by radio-telemetry has been used successfully to research home range and habitat utilisation by Richardson's Merlins in the sagebrush-and-grassland habitats of south-eastern Montana. There three male Merlins had elongated, lozenge-shaped home ranges of 12, 23 and 28 km^2 and travelled up to 9 km from their nests (Becker & Sieg 1987). Tree-nesting and ground-nesting taiga Merlins *Falco c. columbarius* studied in interior Alaska showed the same tendency to range widely. Average foraging flights took three males 3-5 km from the nest. They often made extensive use of alpine slopes and canyons above their forest, nesting areas (Schempf & Titus 1988, Schempf 1989). In 1990, visual observations of early-morning foraging flights away from and prey deliveries to a tree nest containing young, situated 400 m above sea level in the Galloway Forest Park, indicated that **extensive high moorland areas above the forest boundary likewise constitute an important hunting habitat.** It is relevant to note that 43 (47%) of 91 nesting areas found from 1979-89 in north-east Scotland were situated between 400 and 600 m asl (Rebecca *et al.* 1992)

5. 8   OTHER FORAGING AREAS : 1986 - 1987

In south-west Scotland some male Merlins begin to frequent their forest nesting areas during the last days of February (Forest Raptor Project unpubl. data). In March and early April Merlin diets contain a high proportion of passerines associated with farmland and the edges of deciduous woodland and conifer plantations, the Chaffinch being the commonest woodland prey species (Bibby 1987, Parr *in press*). It is well known that mature conifer plantations are a haven for finches (Simms 1976, Shaw 1990, Shaw & Livingstone 1991) and whilst some may be taken above the forest canopy (which Merlins may hunt as if it were a rolling moorland landscape) these and other small woodland birds are more likely to be caught by Merlins hunting along forest edges, in forest glades (Lawrence 1949, Beebe 1974) and also on clearfelled sites and farmland. It was therefore considered important to quantify habitats other than semi-natural grassland and upland heath within 4 km of the nest territory, which could provide prey in the spring pre-laying period as well as later in the breeding season.

A general observation concerning the "minor habitats" summarised in Table 14 is that the habitat features associated with coniferous plantations appeared to provide a greater variety of foraging opportunities for Merlins than the minor habitats present on and near upland farms in Galloway. When considered as a whole, however, it is evident that there was a wide range of non-moorland foraging habitats available within hunting range of all Merlin nesting territories.

Eighteen (90%) pairs had access to more than 20 km of mature forest edge (mainly adjacent to streams, moorland, farmland and/or young conifer plantations); seven of these pairs may also have benefited from prey taken on young restocked sites. Forest glades, chiefly unplanted riparian zones and rides (estimated at 5% of the total coniferous woodland area), were present and extensive within 4 km of each nesting territory as were forest roads. Although only 4 (20%) pairs nested within 1 km of established farmland, limited amounts of enclosed farmland with either scrub, broadleaved trees or hedgerows, were present within 4 km radius of 16 (80%) nest territories.

Table 13. Major habitats within 4 km radius (c. 50 km^2) of Merlin nests (n = 20) in south-west Scotland, 1986-87.

a	b	c		d		e		f		g	
Nest	Nest site type	Grass & heather moor		Young conifer forest		Forest glades		Well-grown conifer forest		Total c, d, e*	
		km^2	%	km^2	%	km^2	%	km^2	%	km^2	%
1	C	33.3	66.2	-	-	0.7	1.4	14.1	28.0	34.0	67.6
2	C	20.1	40.0	10.8	21.4	1.4	2.8	16.8	33.1	32.3	64.2
3	C	20.1	40.0	17.0	33.8	1.5	3.0	11.4	22.6	38.6	76.8
4	C	6.9	13.7	11.8	23.4	2.1	4.2	28.8	57.2	20.8	41.3
5	C	33.8	67.2	0.1	0.2	0.8	1.6	15.1	30.0	34.7	69.0
6	C	35.9	71.4	0.5	1.0	0.7	1.4	12.7	25.2	37.1	73.8
7	C	13.6	27.0	1.1	2.2	1.8	3.6	33.7	67.0	16.5	32.8
8	C	25.2	50.1	-	-	1.2	2.4	23.6	46.9	26.4	52.5
9	C	29.6	58.8	0.6	1.2	0.9	1.8	16.8	33.4	31.1	61.8
10	C	28.6	56.8	6.6	13.1	1.0	2.0	13.0	25.8	36.2	71.9
11	C	30.5	60.6	9.1	18.1	1.0	2.0	9.0	17.9	40.6	80.7
12	C	27.9	55.4	-	-	1.1	2.2	21.2	42.1	29.0	57.6
13	C	34.4	68.4	-	-	0.5	1.0	9.1	18.1	34.9	69.4
14	C	21.4	42.5	0.8	1.6	1.1	2.2	20.6	40.9	23.3	46.3
15	C	26.1	51.9	7.5	14.9	1.2	2.4	14.5	28.8	34.8	69.2
16	C	26.8	53.3	0.8	1.6	1.2	2.4	21.4	42.5	28.8	57.3
17	B	28.2	56.1	6.3	12.5	1.0	2.0	13.1	26.0	35.5	70.6
18	H	39.0	77.6	5.2	10.3	0.5	1.0	5.2	10.3	44.7	88.9
19	H	32.2	64.0	0.6	1.2	0.8	1.6	15.6	31.0	33.6	66.8
20	H	35.5	70.6	9.0	17.9	0.7	1.4	4.5	8.9	45.2	89.9
Average for 17 forest nests		**26.0** % (51.7)		4.3 % (8.5)		1.1 % (2.2)		17.3 % (34.5)		**31.4** % (62.4)	
Average for 3 moorland nests		**35.5** (70.6)		4.9 (9.7)		0.6 (1.2)		8.4 (16.7)		**41.1** (81.7)	
Average for all 20 nests		**27.4** (54.5)		4.4 (8.7)		1.0 (2.0)		16.0 (31.9)		**32.9** (65.4)	

C = nest in conifer; B = stick nest in broadleaved tree; H = ground nest in heather..
Nests 1-17 in conifer plantations; nests 18-20 on moorland.
Column **c** : totals include improved grassland data shown in Appendix 2.
Column **d** combines the first and second rotation, pre-thicket plantation data in Appendix 2.
*Potential foraging areas combined.

Substantial areas (typically > 0.5 km^2 or 50 ha) of prey-rich, pre-thicket conifer forest (1-7 years old) were present within 4 km of 12 (60%) Merlin nests (Table 14, 15 & Appendix 2). Survey records and previous studies by the author showed that male Merlins regularly hunt Meadow Pipits in young conifer plantations from the beginning of April, when male pipits establish their territories and perform elaborate song flights which include periods of hovering and parachuting to the ground. In 1986 three, closely spaced, tree-nesting Merlin pairs bred near an expanse of recently afforested, prey-rich moorland, their mean nearest neighbour distance being 3.2 km.

Table 14. Minor habitats within 4 km (50. 2 km^2) of Merlin nest sites (n = 20) in south-west Scotland, 1986-87.

| | | a | | | b | |
| | No. of | % | Where > | No. of | % |
Habitats	nests			nests	
Improved grassland	16	80	0.50 km^2	11	55
Arable land	16	80	0.10 km^2	6	30
Scrub	13	65	0.05 km^2	10	50
Hedgerows	13	65	1.00 km	9	45
Bloadleaved woodland	15	75	0.10 km^2	8	40
Young conifer forest (1-7 yrs)	13	65	0.50 km^2	12	60
Restocked conifer forest (1-7 yrs)	7	35	0.50 km^2	4	20
Forest glades	20	100	0.50 km^2	20	100
High forest edge*	20	100	20.00 km	18	90
Forest roads	20	100	10.00 km	18	90

* Mainly external, riparian and restock edges; edges along narrow internal forest rides not included.

Table 15 . Distance from Merlin nests in high forest (n = 17) and on moorland (n = 3) to foraging areas in young conifer plantations (1-7 years) in Galloway, 1986-87.

| **Distance** | Nests | | |
metres	No.	%	%
0-250	3	15	
250-500	0	0	
500-1000	2	10	
1000-1500	4	20	*70*
1500-2000	2	10	
2000-2500	2	10	
2500-3000	0	0	
3000-3500	1	5	
No pre-thicket forest within 4 km	6	30	*30*
Total	20	(100)	

(Distance from moorland nests to pre-thicket conifers = 550 m, 1550 m, 3250 m.)

To summarise, in Galloway the preferred Merlin nest sites located in 1986-87 were in closed-canopy coniferous forest adjacent to tracts of grass and heather moorland, with young conifer plantations and/or some established farmland with scrub or broadleaved woodland present within 4 km radius of the nest territory. Analysis of the Galloway habitat data suggests that in south-west Scotland the Merlin's choice of nesting place may be strongly influenced by the availability of prey-rich foraging areas in the pre-laying period (late March and April). In this respect the Merlin may behave somewhat like the Sparrowhawk whose breeding densities in woodland are governed by the food supply in early spring (Newton *et al.* 1986b).

5.9 BREEDING SUCCESS : 1986 - 1987

As the survey protocol emphasised non-disturbance of breeding birds, details of Merlin clutch sizes were not obtained; it is known, however, that most clutches comprise 4 or 5 eggs (see Crick *in press*, Rebecca *et al.* 1992). Repeated prey deliveries to the nest in May, June and early July indicated that 25 (86%) of 29 territorial pairs had laid and were feeding young from mid June. Seven broods of fledged young (1,2,2,2,3,4,5,) were observed in nesting areas in July, yielding an average of 2.7 young per successful pair. If this small sample is representative, then overall productivity in 1986-87 may have been close to the average of 2.5 young per pair considered necessary by Olsson (1980) to maintain population stability. The largest brood of 5 young was seen near a forest edge site close to a recently afforested heather moor. Members of the S.W. Scotland Raptor Study Group, covering some other parts of Strathclyde Region as well as Dumfries & Galloway Region, found 13 pairs in 1987 (Roxburgh 1988) and reported 31 fledged young from 9 clutches (3.4 young per successful pair; 2.4 young per territorial pair).

5.10 MERLIN POPULATION ESTIMATE : 1986 -1987

Merlin populations can achieve high densities where prey and nest sites are plentiful. For instance, in the urban environment (area : 122 km^2) of Saskatoon, Saskatchewan the tree-nesting population of Richardson's Merlin increased from 1 to 16 breeding pairs in only 12 years, between 1971 and 1982 (Oliphant & Haug 1985) and had reached 27 pairs by 1987 (James 1988). In the USSR Galushin (1981) reported " a rather high density in the forest-tundra zone along railways as well as near settlements where crow nests are abundant." In northen England densities of 4 to 6+ pairs/100 km^2 were found in 1983-84 in sixteen 10-km squares containing expanses of heather-dominated moorland but the mean density per occupied square (n = 74) was 2.31 pairs; Merlins were considered to be generally much scarcer in grass-dominated and afforested regions where 1 pair/100 km^2 was more usual (Bibby and Nattrass 1986). The 1987 Galloway survey located 15 pairs in 19 active 10-km squares, a density of 0.8 pairs/100 km^2.

It is important to emphasise that the Galloway Forests Merlin Survey covered *c.* 40% of the afforested land and less than 10% of the "moorland and mountain" ground in the project area. Although the survey workers were asked to record all Merlin sightings within and outside their study areas, it is likely that part of the forest-dwelling population was not found. For example, pairs which failed early could easily have been overlooked. The fact that only 5 territories were recorded as occupied in both years of the survey would strongly suggest that some pairs escaped detection. Moreover, nine moorland areas were not fully explored and additional pairs may have bred in heather or in conifers at the moorland edge. An estimate of 20-25 pairs in 22 active 10-km squares (i.e. 0.9-1.1 pairs/100 km^2) for the Merlin population in this extensively and densely forested project area (with a strong Peregrine presence) in the years 1986-87 might not, therefore, be considered unrealistic.

5.11 SUMMARY OF RAPTOR SURVEYS : 1986 - 1987

The surveys provided information about the distribution of nine species of raptor and two species of owl on afforested lands across south-west Scotland and highlighted the importance of forests as refuges for woodland and upland birds of prey. Figure 15 reflects the abundance of birds of prey and corvids recorded on a presence/absence basis in the 55 forest study areas in 1987.

It is encouraging to note that four species of raptor and two species of owl (Table 16 & Appendix 3) were observed hunting regularly on a number of recently restocked plots (n = 11; average size 1.5 km^2). In addition to Barn Owls which bred in old farm buildings and in tree nestboxes (Shaw & Dowell 1990, Orchel & Shawyer 1992) and Short-eared Owls which nested in dense ground vegetation on the restocked sites, Tawny Owls and Long-eared Owls were also known to be present but because of their nocturnal behaviour did not feature as target species in the survey.

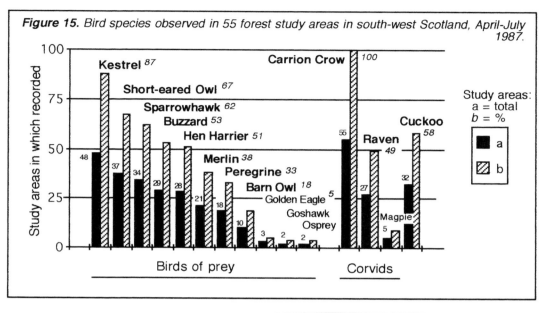

Figure 15. *Bird species observed in 55 forest study areas in south-west Scotland, April-July 1987.*

Table 16. Birds of prey observed hunting on 11 restocked forest sites (1-7 years old) in Galloway, April to July 1987.

Species		Restocked sites No.	%
Kestrel	*Falco tinnunculus*	11	100
Buzzard	*Buteo buteo*	10	91
Sparrowhawk	*Accipiter nisus*	9	82
Short-eared Owl	*Asio flammeus*	5	45
Hen Harrier	*Circus cyaneus*	4	36
Barn Owl	*Tyto alba*	2	18

Of particular interest were the records of Hen Harrier. This moorland species whose British population increased in the years 1945-75 (Watson 1977) now stands at *c.* 600 pairs (most of which breed in Scotland). It is still threatened locally by persecution (Cadbury *et al.* 1988, Everett 1991, RSPB & NCC 1991). Male Hen Harriers often range widely from the nest when foraging, at least 4 to 5 km (Watson 1977, P J Hudson pers. comm.), and are highly conspicuous, which accounts for the species having been observed in 28 (51 %) of 55 study areas in 1987. Personal observations, discussions with observers and close scrutiny of the survey records for breeding evidence such as food passes near the nest, revealed that birds had bred or held territory at 15 locations in thirteen 10-km squares in 1986-87 (Figure 16i) Harriers nested successfully in rank vegetation on heather moorland as well as in mixed patches of heather/bracken/bog myrtle on unplanted and sparsely ground within young plantations (5-20 years old) and they were also seen regularly on some recently restocked sites. For example, in 1987 a cock bird was reported present on the same part of a large clearfell adjacent to heather moorland on ten separate occasions between 4th May and 10th July. Ground nesting on restocked sites in upland forests may occur somewhat more frequently than previously reported (Petty and Anderson 1986; section 5.7 above) and tree-nesting by Hen Harriers, although unusual, should be considered a possibility following the recent discovery of a nest 4.5 m off the ground in a maturing Sitka spruce plantation (also occupied by a pair of Merlins) in Northern Ireland (Scott *et al.* 1991, Watson 1991).

Carrion Crows were very much in evidence in all study areas and could, therefore, have provided stick nests near clearfelled plots for the Merlin. The latter species was seen on two restocked sites but was not found breeding within 1 km of a clearfell in Galloway in 1986-87.

Two upland species, the Buzzard and Raven, considered to be at risk from afforestation of upland foraging areas in Galloway (Stroud 1987, Marquiss *et al.* 1978, Ratcliffe 1990) were well represented throughout the region, with some pairs breeding at new sites in coniferous trees adjacent to sheep-walk as recorded in Wales (Newton, Davis & Davis 1982b). Sparrowhawks, Kestrels, Short-eared Owls and Barn Owls were numerous and widespread and the Golden Eagles frequented their long-established haunts. Osprey and Goshawk were each recorded in two forest study areas.

The species maps (Figure 16), based on the 1986-87 forest surveys and additional data gathered by the author, show the breeding season distribution of raptorial birds in each 10-km square of the Galloway project area. Confirmed and probable breeding are represented by a single "breeding" symbol (large dot) and a small dot indicates that the species was "seen" in suitable breeding habitat. Magpie and Cuckoo data for the region have not been mapped.

The survey findings clearly indicate that the extensive, restructured forests now being created in south-west Scotland can provide nesting and foraging habitats for thriving raptor communities. These include the Merlin and Hen Harrier which were found as forest-nesting birds in districts containing substantial areas of pre-thicket forest, heather-dominated moorland and grassy sheep-walk over which they chiefly foraged.

Figure 16. Breeding distribution of 12 bird species in 10-km grid squares throughout the Galloway project area, 1986-87.

Figure 16a. Barn Owl

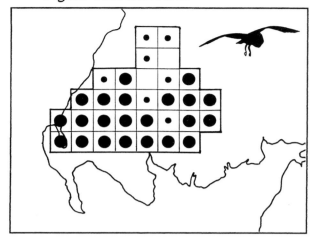

Status : common, 100-120 pairs; 5+ pairs in twelve 10-km squares.

Nest site : lays on ledges, in nestboxes and sometimes among hay bales in farm buildings; also nests in cavities and chimneys of derelict cottages; occupies nestboxes placed in trees at plantation edges; occasionally found in cavities in deciduous trees and cliffs.

Foraging habitat : rough grassland on farms, usually below 200 m; pre-thicket plantations (1st and 2nd rotation) and forest edges and glades; marshland.

Figure 16b. Short-eared Owl

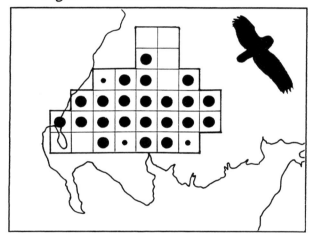

Status : common, 100-200 pairs; numbers fluctuate; 20+ pairs in some 10-km squares in peak vole years.

Nest site : usually in rank ground vegetation (heather, bracken, grass, rushes) in a pre-thicket plantation (first and second rotation); occasionally on heather moorland.

Foraging habitat : pre-thicket conifer plantations and moorland

Figure 16c. Kestrel

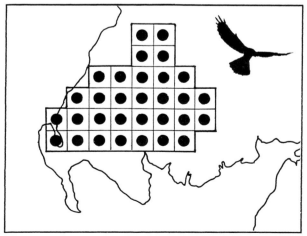

Status : widespread and locally very common, probably 250-500 pairs; 20+ pairs in some 10-km squares;

Nest site : uses old corvid nests in mature plantations and deciduous woodland; lays on ledges in derelict and occupied buildings, crags and quarries; also lays among hay bales and in nestboxes in farm buildings; occasionally nests in deciduous tree cavities.

Foraging habitat : farmland, grass and heather moorland, pre-thicket conifer plantations, forest edges and glades; parkland and urban fringes.

● breeding   • seen

Figure 16d. Peregrine

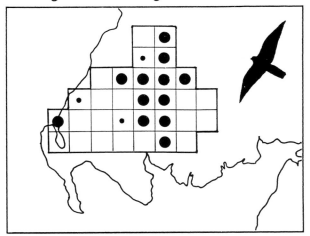

Status : uncommon, 25-30 pairs.

Nest site : lays on cliff ledges and in old Raven nests on crags.

Foraging habitat : pigeon flightlines through hills, above plantations and along coast; moorland; unplanted ground in upland forests; occasionally hunts pre-thicket plantations and edges of restocked sites.

Figure 16e. Buzzard

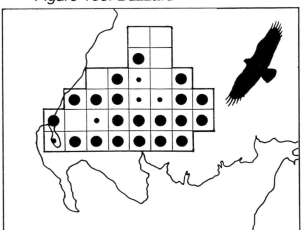

Status : fairly common, about 70 pairs; population expanding slowly as first rotation plantations are felled and restructured; 5+ pairs in some 10-km squares.

Nest site : builds large stick nests in mature deciduous and coniferous woodland; formerly nested on crags.

Foraging habitat : sheepwalk, heather moorland, woodland glades and edges, pre-thicket plantations, open deciduous forest and lowland farms.

Figure 16f. Golden Eagle

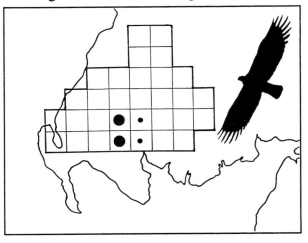

Status : rare, 2-3 breeding pairs.

Nest site : constructs very large stick nests in open coniferous woodland and on steep cliffs.

Foraging habitat : montane and sub-montane heather / grass moorland; open ground in coniferous woodland.

(Two dots have been moved by up to two 10-km squares.)

● breeding   • seen

Figure 16g. Sparrowhawk

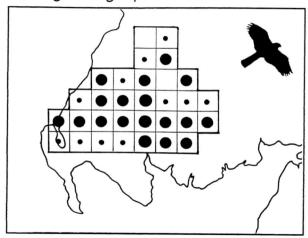

Status : common, estimated 200-250 pairs; 5-10 pairs in some extensively forested 10-km squares; numbers highest in squares containing a patchwork of farmland and mixed-age woodland.

Nest site : builds stick nests in closed-canopy coniferous plantations, shelterbelts and copses, usually below 300 m; occasionally nests in deciduous woodland.

Foraging habitat : young and mixed-age conifer plantations, farmland with copses, scrub and hedgerows; deciduous woodland, moorland, parkland and urban fringes.

Figure 16h. Goshawk

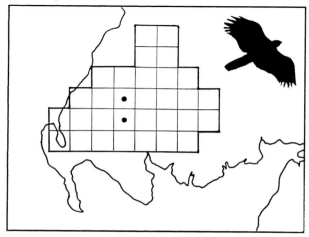

Status : rare, 2-3 territories occupied in 1986-87; numbers increasing. (Five territories occupied in 1990.)

Nest site : constructs large stick nests, usually in mature coniferous woodland (tree height > 12 m).

Foraging habitat : mature plantation edges and forest glades ; farmland and moorland close to forest perimeter; small woods.

(The dots have been moved by up to two 10-km squares.)

Figure 16i. Hen Harrier

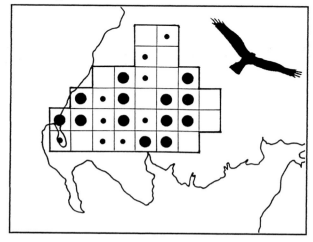

Status : scarce, 12-15 pairs.

Nest site : makes nest of heather twigs and dried grass in rank ground vegetation (among heather, bog myrtle, rushes, purple moor grass, bracken) on moorland and in pre-thicket and thicket plantations.

Foraging habitat : moorland, young plantations and recently restocked forest sites; unplanted ground in forests; marginal farmland; marshland.

● breeding   • seen

Figure 16j. Osprey

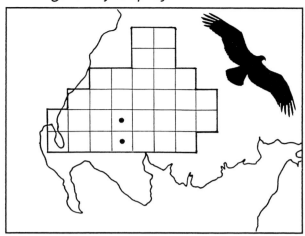

Status : rare, 2 territories occupied.

Nest site : builds stick nests in tall conifers close to water; occupies nesting platforms sited in mature plantations.

Foraging habitat : lochs, fish farms, rivers, estuaries.

(The dots have been moved by up to three 10-km squares.)

Figure 16k. Carrion Crow

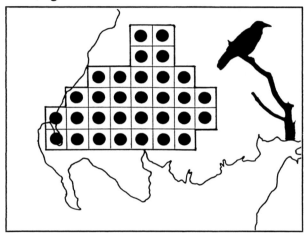

Status : widespread and locally very common; probably 50-200+ pairs in some 10-km squares covering valleys containing a patchwork of coniferous woodland, sheep-walk and mixed farmland.

Nest site : stick nests built near coniferous woodland edge, in deciduous woodland or in isolated moorland, parkland or urban trees; occasionally builds on crag ledges.

Foraging habitat : sheep-walk, heather moorland, young plantations, mixed farmland; parks, urban wasteland and refuse tips.

Figure 16l. Raven

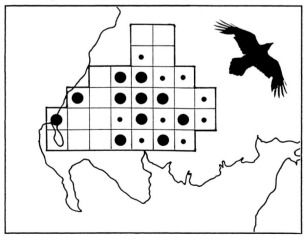

Status : uncommon, about 20 breeding pairs;

Nest site : builds stick nests on cliff ledges; also nests in tall trees at edge of plantations and in isolated woods.

Foraging habitat : sheep-walk and heather moorland; young and mixed-age plantations.

● breeding   • seen

5. 12   MERLINS AND HEN HARRIERS NESTING ON
A RESTOCKED FOREST SITE : 1989 & 1990

The 1986-87 Galloway study areas included eleven substantial restocked forest sites (mean area 1.5 km^2 ; range 0.25 - 2.9 km^2) none of which was selected by Merlins as a breeding territory, although single birds were seen flying low (hunting?) on two restocked sites in early April 1987. However, in 1989 a pair did nest successfully on a 1.7 km^2 plot of restocked ground within a major forest complex in S. Scotland (Ronnie Rose Sr., pers. comm.).

The plot is situated at 365-455 m above sea level on a south-west facing slope and is surrounded on three sides by extensive, thicket and pole-stage conifer plantations. To the north there is an unplanted grassy ridge with heather *Calluna* locally dominant ; beyond the ridge lie pre-thicket and closed-canopy plantations. A crop of 15-year-old Lodgepole pine (of inappropriate genetic origin) was prematurely felled on the plot in 1986 and the site was restocked in 1987 with a mixture of Sitka spruce and Lodgepole pine. The plot is covered with patches of rank heather, particularly along rides, streamsides and in deer control areas. Stunted pines have been left in places to act as fraying posts for Roe Deer and four small blocks of unthinned woodland (total area *circa* 12 ha) have also been retained.

The Merlins nested at 425 m in a patch of rank heather within the young forest about 250 m from the top edge of the plot and 1500 m from the nearest external forest boundary. The main foraging areas available to the pair were two large enclaves of lower lying, recently afforested, prey-rich grass moorland beyond the ridge to the north and north-west (area 5.5 km^2 and 8 km^2 respectively) and a large area (10+ km^2) of unimproved pasture lying below a belt of well-grown forest to the south. The distances to the main pre-thicket foraging areas were 1.8 km and 2.4 km respectively and the distance to sheep-walk was 1.5 km. The nesting area was connected to the enclaves of young forest by a network of broad, grassy fire-breaks (some more than 100 metres wide) .

The nesting territory is shown in Figure17 and an analysis of the main habitat types within 1 km, 4 km and 5 km radius of the Merlin nest is given in Table 17. Within 1 km of the nest, *c.* 2 km^2 (200 ha) or 64% of the land could be classified as "open ground" i.e. unplanted hill land and early pre-thicket forest. The amount of "open ground" foraging habitat available within 4 km and 5 km of the nest was 18.3 km^2 and 29.5 km^2 respectively, of which only 4.3 km^2 and 9.6 km^2 respectively was unimproved grassland.

The pair reared three young and the male was observed regularly in June, July and early August, carrying prey towards the nest site from the north, north-west and south. Food passes took place near the hilltop fence-posts of the plot and the fledged young were frequently fed by the forest road within 150 m of the nest site. The Merlins shared their territory with three pairs of Short-eared Owls, all of which reared young. In 1990 the Merlins were absent but one cock Hen Harrier and two females were present. Two harrier nests, situated approximately 800 m apart, were recorded on the site. One nest failed early but the other produced five young (Ronnie Rose Jr., pers. comm.). The attraction of this restocked site for birds of prey was evident again the following spring. On the evening of 8th April 1991 Meadow Pipits were in abundance, Short-tailed Field Vole runs were widespread and voles were active; a grey cock Hen Harrier was displaying over a knoll and quartering the ground; two Short-eared Owls and a female Hen Harrier were also hunting.

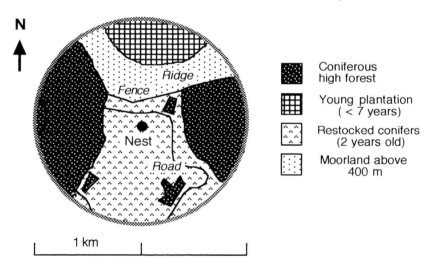

Figure 17. The major habitats within 1 km radius (3.1 km²) of a Merlin nest on a restocked forest site in the central Southern Uplands, 1989.

Table 17. Main habitat types within radii of 1 km (3.1 km^2), 4 km (50.2 km^2) and 5 km (78.5 km^2) of a Merlin nest on a restocked forest site in the central Southern Uplands, 1989. (A pair of Hen Harriers nested successfully on the site in 1990.)

Main Habitats	Within 1 km km^2	%	Within 4 km km^2	%	Within 5 km km^2	%
1. Heather moor	0.16	5.1	1.25	2.5	1.55	2.0
2. Grass moor	0.30	9.6	3.10	6.2	8.10	10.3
3. Young conifer forest (1-7 yrs)	0.28	8.9	8.18	16.3	12.14	15.5
4. Restocked conifers (1-7 yrs)	1.08	34.4	1.58	3.1	1.58	2.0
5. Young broadleaves	0.03	1.0	0.98	1.9	1.39	1.8
6. Forest glades	0.18	5.7	3.21	6.4	4.82	6.1
7. Well-grown conifers (8-30 yrs)	1.10	35.0	31.85	63.3	48.78	62.1
8. Water (lochs, streams, ponds)	< 0.01	0.3	c.0.13	0.3	c.0.21	0.3
Total	3.14	(100)	50.28	(100)	78.57	(100)

Linear features	km		km		km	
9. Forest roads	4.0		120-130		170-180	
10. Mature forest edge (as Table 16)	5.0		> 40		> 65	

Potential foraging areas	km2	%	km2	%	km2	%
a. Unafforested hill land (1,2)	0.46	14.6	4.35	8.6	9.65	12.3
b. Newly planted forest (3,5)	0.31	9.9	9.16	18.2	13.53	17.2
c. Young replanted forest (4)	1.08	34.4	1.58	3.1	1.58	2.0
d. Forest glades (6)	0.18	5.7	3.21	6.4	4.82	6.1
Total	**2.03**	**(64.6)**	**18.30**	**(36.3)**	**29.58**	**(37.6)**

6   DISCUSSION

6. 1   RECENT POPULATION TRENDS IN GALLOWAY AND OTHER REGIONS
In 1984 Ian Newton considered that the Merlin was the only regularly breeding
diurnal raptor whose numbers were declining in the British Isles (BTO News, No.
131). From the1950s to the early 1980s declines in Merlin populations were
reported in several areas : Wales (Roberts & Green 1983, Bibby 1986), the Peak
District (Newton *et al.* 1981), Northumbria (Newton *et al.* 1986a) and Orkney (Meek
1988). In the absence of data from rigorous population studies it was suggested that
declining numbers might be associated with poor breeding production, in other
words with "production of insufficient young to offset... adult mortality" (Newton
et al. 1986a, Bibby 1986). In the above and other relevant studies (including Newton
et al. 1982a, Newton & Haas 1988) a number of contributory factors were discussed:
a) widespread contamination of Merlin eggs with organochlorine insecticide residues
and mercury, [113, 125, 128, 131, 133]
b) increased natural predation, [113, 131]
c) human disturbance, persecution and nest robbing, [14, 113, 131, 133, 184]
d) loss of moorland breeding habitat resulting from extensive afforestation, [14, 113, 184]
e) degradation and loss of heather moorland breeding habitat caused by uncontrolled
burning, over grazing and agricultural improvement, [14, 113, 184]
f) inclement weather in the pre-laying, incubation and early nestling period.[113, 184]

In a long-term study in Northumbria, where patterns of land use are not unlike those
in Galloway, it was noted that traditional Merlin nesting places (mainly on the
ground) within young plantations were abandoned in the late 1970s-early 1980s
(Newton, Meek & Little 1986). During this period, when the British Peregrine and
Sparrowhawk populations were recovering from insecticide-related declines
(Ratcliffe 1980, Newton & Haas 1984), the breeding performance of the remaining
intensively monitored, ground-nesting, moorland Merlin population deteriorated and
breeding numbers also apparently decreased. The researchers attributed progressive
breeding failure and population decline on moorland to the increasing predation of
nest contents by Foxes and other predators including man, as well as to the presence
of toxic chemicals in Merlin eggs which together may have "shifted the balance
between breeding and mortality rates". It was claimed that "all likely-looking sites
around known breeding area were searched". From 1979-83 a few tree-nesting pairs
were found in conifer plantations; yet, if systematic and painstaking searches of
mature forest edges had been conducted in late June and early July a different picture
of overall population trends may well have emerged.

A similar story of poor breeding success and apparent population decline was
reported in Wales by Colin Bibby (1986) who suggested that " the ultimate cause

may be declining habitat suitablity whether the proximate causes of nesting failure are predators or food shortage." Although Bibby had located a number of forest nesting pairs as had Newton *et al*. (1986a), his study focused mainly on traditional moorland nesting places and their abandonment by Merlins in areas where conversion of heather to grass by agricultural improvement and/or overgrazing had been significant. His hypothesis that Merlins prefer heather-dominated to grass-dominated moorland though plausible was problematic for Merlins occur in grass-dominated landscapes throughout their breeding range in Britain and Ireland, North America and Central Asia. Moreover, in Britain preferred prey species and their densities are comparable on heather moorland and semi-natural grassland, as Bibby himself remarked.

The most recent Merlin studies in Welsh forests and in Kielder Forest District have revealed a pattern of nesting near the forest edge close to unimproved grassland and heather moor (C J Bibby pers. comm., Parr 1991, Little & Davison 1992) similar to that discovered in Galloway, which must call into question much of the speculation by Newton *et al*. (1986a) and Bibby (1986) concerning the marked population declines reported in the latter regions several years ago. Furthermore, breeding success and numbers have recently begun to improve in Orkney (Benn 1991) and the South Pennine population believed to have been stricken by pesticides in the 1950s-60s has begun to recover (P Denton pers. comm., Haworth & Fielding 1988, Crick *in press*). In part of north-east Scotland (Grampian Region excluding Moray District) during the 1980s a population of 30-50 pairs breeding mainly on managed heather moorland showed no apparent signs of decline, with 211 (64%) of 328 monitored pairs rearing one or more young to flying (Rebecca *et al*. 1992); and in the Shetland Isles Merlin numbers have remained relatively stable over the past 12 years (Ellis & Okill 1990, Benn 1991).

In Galloway the loss of moorland breeding habitat to forestry in the 1960s and 1970s was more rapid and widespread than in Northumbria (Avery & Leslie 1990) where tracts of heather moorland continued to be preserved and in many instances managed for sporting purposes. Between 1950 and 1975 in south-west Scotland much of the least productive ground for sheep and that traditionally most favoured as nesting habitat by Merlins (i.e. heather moorland) was afforested. In the 1970s and early 1980s as the trees grew and canopy closed, open country bird communities (i.e. preferred prey species) virtually disappeared from vast stretches of dense, even-aged forest and Merlins abandoned most of their breeding haunts on fragments of heather moor within these plantations.

At the same time as the Fox and corvid populations were increasing in the young forests (Staines 1986, Petty 1985b, Hewson & Kolb 1974) many of the remaining heather moors were subjected to annual large-scale burning to improve pasture for sheep; consequently, nesting cover diminished, leaving the remaining ground-nesting moorland Merlins more vulnerable to inclement weather and disturbance by predators. This was perhaps reflected in the recorded decline in the use of traditional moorland sites (Figure 10).

However, in the absence of detailed information on breeding performance from a large number of territories, one cannot judge whether the decline in the use of traditional heather sites inside forests and on adjacent moorland was linked to widespread breeding failure and consequent population decrease as suggested in Northumbria by Newton *et al.* (1986a). Whilst there is some evidence of nest predation (Table 6), the role of organochlorine compounds and other pollutants in depressing breeding performance in Galloway Merlins is far from proven (Newton & Haas 1988).

A more natural explanation in keeping with local records of site use is that birds were spatially and temporally displaced from many traditional nesting slopes within plantations as well as from sites on nearby heather moorland as a consequence of widespread habitat changes - chiefly because of large-scale afforestation of nearby moorland foraging areas. Disturbance by ground predators and competition for territory from increasing numbers of Peregrines and possibly Sparrowhawks (Rebecca 1990, Rebecca *et al.* 1992, Weir 1984) may also have hastened the abandonment of a number of long-established nesting places though the evidence for this is limited and largely circumstantial.

Most significant, however, is the fact that Merlins continued to breed on the less extensively burned, larger moors in south-west Scotland and began to use secure nest sites in coniferous trees as soon as these sites became available, certainly by the early 1980s and possibly earlier. These tree nests were generally situated near the forest edge close to grass and heather moorland and young plantations and were located in moderately afforested districts i.e where the average coniferous woodland cover within 4 km radius of the nest was less than 46% (Table 13, Figure 20 & 22).

The sole base-line for the Galloway Merlin population dates from the *BTO Atlas* years 1968-72 when, over the five years of study, Merlins were recorded during the breeding season in 22 (71%) of the 31 x 10-km squares surveyed in 1986-87. Unfortunately, comprehensive data about the annual frequency of site occupancy during the *Atlas* period were not recorded. However, judging by the available records and taking into consideration the vast area of moorland and pre-thicket foraging habitat available at that time, the Merlin population in the project area may well have totalled 30-35 pairs; the species was possibly as numerous as during the grouse shooting heyday of the late nineteenth century. By 1986-87, as suggested earlier, notwithstanding the occupation of new forest edge sites, the population had probably declined moderately to 20-25 pairs as many of the former moorland and pre-thicket foraging areas had been converted to dense and extensive coniferous forest.

In view of the very recent afforestation of moorland in the project area (which will provide temporary concentrations of preferred prey species in pre-thicket plantations) the Galloway Merlin population may be able to maintain its present level or even increase somewhat during the 1990s by establishing new nest territories in maturing plantations as occurred in parts of Kielder Forest from 1986 to 1990 (Little and Davison 1992); but the possibility cannot be discounted that in due course, owing to loss of moorland foraging habitat to forestry, Merlin numbers will decline further before eventually stabilising at a lower level.

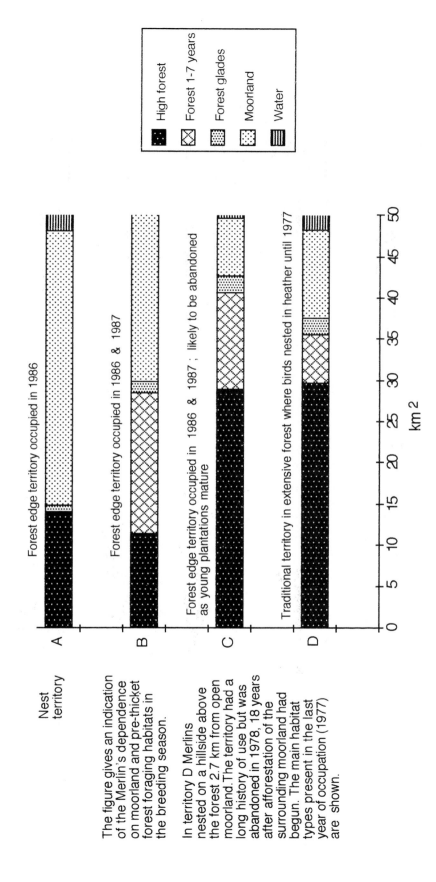

Figure 18. *Proportions of major habitats within 4 km radius (c.50 km²) of 4 Merlin nesting territories in conifer plantations in south-west Scotland.*

Nest territory

A Forest edge territory occupied in 1986

The figure gives an indication of the Merlin's dependence on moorland and pre-thicket forest foraging habitats in the breeding season.

B Forest edge territory occupied in 1986 & 1987

C Forest edge territory occupied in 1986 & 1987 ; likely to be abandoned as young plantations mature

In territory D Merlins nested on a hillside above the forest 2.7 km from open moorland. The territory had a long history of use but was abandoned in 1978, 18 years after afforestation of the surrounding moorland had begun. The main habitat types present in the last year of occupation (1977) are shown.

D Traditional territory in extensive forest where birds nested in heather until 1977

km²

High forest
Forest 1-7 years
Forest glades
Moorland
Water

73

Figure 19. *Distribution of major habitats surrounding tree-nest A of Merlin in coniferous high forest in south-west Scotland, 1986.*

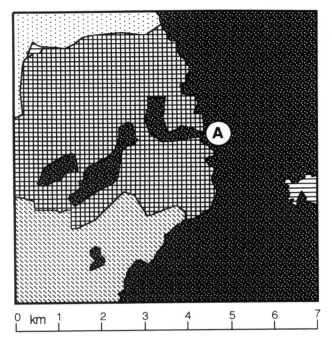

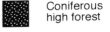 Coniferous high forest

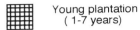 Young plantation (1-7 years)

Moorland below 250 m

Moorland above 250 m

Freshwater lochs

A Merlin breeding area regularly occupied since the early 1900s and associated in 1986-87 with newly afforested heather moorland, an ephemeral prey-rich habitat where Meadow Pipit densities were 50 to 100 pairs per 100 km^2 . Moorland foraging habitat is diminishing rapidly in this district and several pairs of forest Merlins are likely to be displaced.

Figure 20. *Distribution of major habitats surrounding tree-nest B of Merlin in coniferous high forest in south-west Scotland, 1986.*

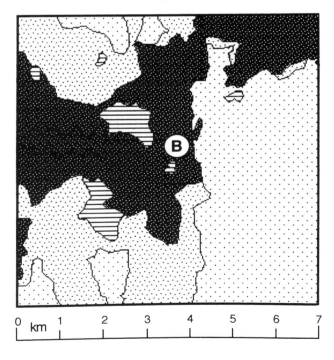

 Coniferous high forest

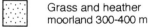 Grass and heather moorland 300-400 m

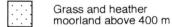 Grass and heather moorland above 400 m

Freshwater lochs

A Merlin nesting area associated with an expanse of high-level moorland in the western Southern Uplands.

Figure 21. *Distribution of major habitats surrounding tree-nest C of Merlin in coniferous high forest in south-west Scotland, 1988.*

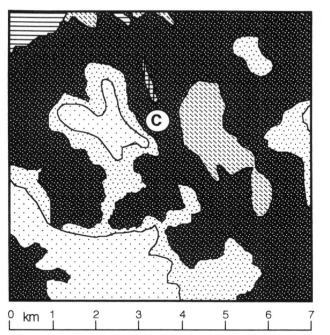

■ Coniferous high forest

▦ Young plantation (< 3 years)

▨ Grass and heather moorland below 250 m

⬚ Grass and heather moorland 250-400 m

⬚ Grass and heather moorland above 400 m

▤ Freshwater loch

A Merlin nesting area in an extensive patchwork of high- and low-level moorland maintained by periodic burning and regular grazing by sheep, feral goats and deer. Meadow Pipits, Wheatears and Chaffinches were the main prey species brought to this nest. Mature forest edges (about 75 km within 4 km radius of the nest site) were an important feature of this pair's hunting range.

Figure 22. *Distribution of major habitats surrounding tree-nest D of Merlin in coniferous high forest in south-west Scotland, 1986.*

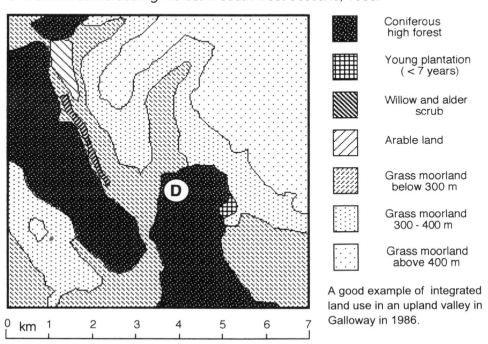

■ Coniferous high forest

▦ Young plantation (< 7 years)

▧ Willow and alder scrub

▧ Arable land

▨ Grass moorland below 300 m

⬚ Grass moorland 300 - 400 m

⬚ Grass moorland above 400 m

A good example of integrated land use in an upland valley in Galloway in 1986.

Forest cover is extensive, landscape values are preserved and moorland blocks remain large enough to support hill sheep farming and breeding Merlins. (The balance between woodland and open ground altered significantly in 1990-91 when more of the sheep-walk between 250 and 400 m was afforested.)

6. 2   ASSOCIATION OF MERLINS AND CROWS

The association of Merlins and corvids is a widespread phenomenon which perhaps evolved in distant, prehistoric times. That the link is strong cannot be denied for this behaviour is not restricted to wooded areas. For example, in Shetland, which is virtually devoid of woodland cover and where Hooded Crows nest on the ground in heather, 51% of Merlin pairs studied from 1984 to 1987 bred in old stick nests of Hooded Crows, presumably because the crows had selected some of the most sheltered nesting sites available to them in deep heather on hillsides (Okill *et al.* 1980, Ellis & Okill 1990).

Tree nesting near forest margins in virgin wilderness is typical of Merlin populations in N. America and N. Europe (Beebe 1974, Laing 1985, Dementiev & Gladkov 1951). Today forest Merlins in Galloway rely heavily on the stick nests of Carrion Crows which are more numerous than those of other potential nest providers like the Magpie, Buzzard and Sparrowhawk. Crow territories appear to be fairly regularly spaced along the forest perimeter and seem to be most abundant in plantations adjacent to sheepwalk. For example, in 1987 seven Carrion Crow territories were located by the author along 2 km of forest edge in one upland valley in west Galloway where Merlins bred successfully, hunting over adjacent unimproved sheep pasture. The conspicuous, spring time, nest-building activities of these corvids probably direct Merlins to potential nest sites within forestry plantations.

In N.E. Scotland, Nick Picozzi found that in woodland, Carrion/Hooded Crow nests were usually built "high in the crown (of trees) and inconspicuous from the ground; all provided a clear view." The same nesting areas were occupied from year to year and the nests, which were long-lasting (5-10 years), formed distinct groups. Most crows nested "within 100 metres of the woodland edge and often in a corner; and those further in the wood were always close to a ride or clearing" (Picozzi 1975a).

The majority (n = 10 or 59%) of 17 Merlin tree sites located in Galloway in 1986-87 were less than 200 metres from the forest edge and most were situated in the canopy and close to an opening in the forest. Three widely spaced pairs nested in the same compartments (though not in the same nest trees) in consecutive years. Fidelity to specific forest nesting areas would appear to be an important characteristic of some Merlin pairs in Galloway and in Wales (Parr 1991). As previously suggested, this phenomenon may in part be related to prey abundance in nearby foraging areas since there is clearly no shortage of crow nests for Merlins to occupy in conifer forests from the late pre-thicket stage.

In Kielder Forest the widely publicised siting of 150+ artificial nesting platforms at 500 m intervals along the forest perimeter, has failed to benefit the Merlin population there. As in Galloway, there is an abundance of old corvid nests within coniferous plantations at Kielder which Merlins and Kestrels prefer to utilise (Petty 1985a, Rebecca, Payne & Canham 1991, D Jardine pers comm., Little & Davison 1992). By contrast, in Perthshire Rebecca and Payne have demonstrated that a highly selective approach to placement of artificial nests may occasionally prove effective. For instance, Merlins can be encouraged to re-occupy traditional nesting areas on overgrazed moorland by the provision of nesting platforms in isolated groups of broadleaved trees. This technique (see Appendix 4) may also prove useful on grouse moors where corvid nests and their occupants are routinely destroyed.

Since tree nesting in conifers is now very much the norm in Galloway and throughout the Border Forest Park, Cambrian Mountains and Brecon Beacons National Park, one can safely predict that restoration of forest cover in many other parts of the British uplands will enable the Merlin to exploit new nesting and foraging opportunities, possibly with enhanced breeding success in certain localities; high productivity was noted with Merlins occupying small coniferous copses/shelterbelts on Northumbrian sheep-walks during the 1970s (Newton *et al*. 1978) and more recently tree-nesting pairs in Kielder Forest have been generally more productive than ground nesters (Little & Davison 1992).

The Merlin's preference for utilising corvid nests in maturing conifer plantations will not, however, guarantee its survival in extensively afforested districts where moorland foraging areas of established forest-nesting pairs have recently been planted up or are destined for further large-scale afforestation (see Figure 18).

6.3   THE REQUIREMENTS OF MERLINS BREEDING IN
MIXED-AGE FORESTS

The dynamic, mixed-age character of restructured Scottish forests as evidenced in Galloway is already proving beneficial to raptors by providing new nesting and foraging areas on felled and restocked sites as well as furnishing nesting places in mature conifers within forests (see Section 5.12). Shorter rotations, characterised by relatively large areas of forest in early stages of growth, can be expected in many upland forests where trees are subject to windthrow (Staines 1986, Hibberd 1985). How is the Merlin likely to exploit these nesting and foraging opportunities?

Four factors are likely to influence choice of forest nesting territory :
a) availability of corvid nests and/or heather-covered nesting slopes,
b) abundance and availability of preferred prey species in forest glades, on restocked plots, at the woodland edge and on nearby agricultural land,
c) proximity, size, structure and continuity of moorland foraging areas,
d) avoidance of large predatory birds.

The Galloway data show that Carrion Crow territories are common along forest edges and next to restocked plots; and heathery knolls and slopes within and above the forest are plentiful; therefore, nest sites are unlikely to be a limiting factor.

With regard to the second pre-requisite (prey), male Merlins are known to hunt small woodland birds, particularly in the pre-laying period. These species are available at forest edges along watercourses, roads, deer glades, meadows, farmland, rides, fire-breaks and clearfelled sites (Hill 1983). As the forest structure is modified through felling and restocking, so the length of mature forest edge and potential Merlin foraging habitat increases markedly.

It is also important to note that songbird populations on restocked sites are more abundant and species rich than avian prey populations on newly afforested ground (Currie & Bamford 1981, Bibby *et al.* 1985). Whilst scrub-nesting birds colonise many restocked sites, some replanted areas also attract Meadow Pipits, the preferred open country prey species of the Merlin (Leslie 1981). During the breeding season some restocked sites and forest glades are likely to supply prey for this small falcon.

It must be borne in mind, however, that the large amounts of brash (lop and top) and the luxuriant vegetation so typical of many restocked sites may prevent Merlins from hunting as effectively as they do over the shorter vegetation of sheep-walk, blanket bogs and managed heather moorland. Moreover, since restocked sites (1-7 years old) suitable as Merlin foraging habitat will probably cover no more than 10-15% of the total forest area at any one time (Hibberd 1985, Ratcliffe & Petty 1986), they are likely to provide a supplement to, rather than a substitute for, the Merlin's preferred moorland foraging areas which need to be extensive.

The retention of low-lying agricultural land comprising unimproved or semi-improved pastures and haymeadows within or adjacent to the forest can benefit the Merlin by providing nesting habitat for open country birds as well as foraging habitat for small woodland species (O'Connor & Shrubb 1986, Petty & Avery 1990). Such prey-rich areas are considered to be important hunting places for Merlins in the critical pre-laying period and merit careful management. The proximity of preferred moorland sites to established farmland was noted in Wales by Bibby (1986).

The presence of increasing numbers of Peregrines as well as forest-dwelling Goshawks and Sparrowhawks which hunt on restocked sites, along forest edges and on nearby moorland, and are known predators of the Merlin (Petty 1989, Petty & Anderson 1990, Parr *in press*) may also exert considerable influence on the bird's choice of nesting territory and its foraging behaviour. Resident Peregrines and Goshawks nest much earlier in the year than the semi-resident Merlin. Avoidance of the larger raptors including territorial female Sparrowhawks (Weir 1984, Newton 1986) may in part account for the Merlin's absence from some apparently suitable traditional nesting territories within coniferous forests close to fragmented moorland areas of moderate size (see Table 12). The impact of increased avian and ground predator activity on prey populations nesting on fragments of unmanaged moorland surrounded by mature conifer plantations may also influence the Merlin to select nesting places closer to larger moorland areas where prey may be more abundant and more easily caught.

In view of the bird's requirements for a secure nest site and extensive and productive moorland and forest-edge foraging areas, it is probable that the majority of Merlin nests in restructured forests will continue to be located in well-grown trees near forest-moorland perimeters as well as in stands of mature conifers associated with large enclaves of unplanted ground *which can be maintained by controlled burning and grazing i.e. by traditional moorland management methods* (Figure 20).

Nevertheless, whilst the Galloway habitat data reveal retention of a patchwork of large, closely spaced moorland blocks (typically 8 to 20+ km^2) to be a prerequisite for conservation of Merlin populations in extensively afforested districts, it is to be hoped that the ongoing programme of restructuring in Scottish forests (with grants available for creating open ground habitats to a limit of 20%) will eventually create sufficient additional foraging habitat within the forest perimeter to allow new Merlin territories to become established, possibly close to moorland foraging areas which currently appear marginal.

Nesting on and near large restocked forest sites adjacent to moorland may well become a more frequent occurrence throughout the Scottish uplands. The fact that Merlins have recently begun to nest in new conifer plantations close to high-level moorland plateaux in the Galloway Hills and Cambrian Mountains is encouraging proof of the species' adaptability.

6.4 POTENTIAL IMPACTS OF FORESTRY OPERATIONS, PREDATION AND DISTURBANCE.

Merlin populations can be affected directly through mortality of adults and nestlings (e.g see reference to persecution by Gladstone in Section 3.2), or indirectly through long-term habitat loss and degradation, increased stress, reproductive decline and failure. In Galloway and similarly afforested areas direct mortality may occasionally occur during harvesting operations if nests and nestlings are inadvertently destroyed. **The most serious impacts of forestry operations, however, are likely to occur indirectly, from loss of moorland foraging habitat, clearfelling of preferred nesting areas and increased human disturbance.** Displacement of breeding birds from preferred nesting areas, whatever the cause, may lead to increased competition for limited food resources eventually resulting in a reduction in breeding numbers as suggested by Becker and Ball (1983) and witnessed in part of the Galloway project area over the past 15 years (see Figure 7).

Increased human disturbance of birds on and near afforested lands during the breeding season may arise from 1) greater frequency of harvesting as forests mature, 2) improved public access and 3) pressure from professional and amateur ornithologists for more intensive and widespread raptor studies in Scotland (see below in this section). **The potential problems associated with increased human disturbance of nesting birds of prey have been described minutely by Fyfe and Olendorff (1976). These include nest desertion and damage to eggs and young by frightened adults; cooling, overheating and loss of moisture from eggs; chill and heat prostration of nestlings; missed feedings; premature fledging and increased nest predation.**

In the early stages of the forest cycle Merlins generally nest in rank heather. It is also a well-known fact that **ground-nesting Merlins, whose nests are monitored regularly during the breeding season, are particularly vulnerable to Foxes and other mammalian predators. Scent trails laid down by hill walkers, ornithologists, deer stalkers and forestry workers may pose a serious threat to eggs and young, particularly on moorland enclaves. In addition, Merlin clutches are sometimes destroyed by Carrion/Hooded Crows which are highly observant and skilled nest robbers** (Picozzi 1975b, Wiklund 1979, Newton *et al*. 1986a, Meek 1988, Avery *et al*. 1989, Rebecca 1990, Rebecca *et al*. 1992). The risks to ground-nesting Merlins, as to other moorland birds, may be greater on and near afforested land especially if predator control is relaxed following afforestation (when Fox numbers rise sharply in response to increased Field Vole numbers) and traditional management of moorland vegetation is allowed to lapse (Hewson & Kolb 1974, Hewson & Leitch 1983, Staines 1986, NCC 1986, Thompson *et al.* 1988, Stroud *et al.* 1990, Mitchell & Straker-Smith 1991). In Kielder Forest, where a number of Merlins still nest on the ground at traditional sites, the mean brood size of 106 ground-nests found in the period 1978-90 was only 1.14 young / nest, which was significantly lower than the average of 1.94 fledged young per forest tree-nest (n = 52); the mean clutch sizes at forest ground-sites and forest tree-sites were virtually identical i.e. 3.94 and 4.00 eggs respectively (Little and Davison 1992).

In Galloway Merlins have successfully adapted to the new forest environment by largely switching from nesting on the ground in heather to breeding in stick nests at the edge of coniferous woodlands, ranging in size from small copses (< 5 ha) to plantations covering more than a thousand hectares. **Although these forest nest sites provide breeding Merlins with shelter from inclement weather and greater security from mammalian predators, the forest environment may not be entirely benign since the presence of increasing numbers of large forest raptors may pose a threat to small forest-nesting falcons and hawks** (Newton 1986, Petty 1989, Petty and Anderson 1990, Parr *in press*). At forest tree sites, incubating or brooding females frequently remain silent on the nest until the observer is close at hand and some birds only leave the nest when the nest tree is being climbed (Trimble 1975, Orchel unpubl.). **When flushed from the nest, however, hen Merlins are invariably aggressive and noisy** (e.g. see Newton *et al.* 1978, Smith 1978) **and their alarm calls may draw attention to the nest site, thus increasing the risk of natural predation. The same applies to ground-nesting pairs.**

The relatively low breeding success (typically < 2.2 fledged young / nesting pair) and high rates of nest failure (30-50%) recorded in several ongoing long-term British Merlin studies e.g. in Wales, Northumberland and parts of Scotland have been variously attributed to natural predation, toxic chemicals in the food chain, deterioration of breeding habitat, the effects of inclement weather, human disturbance and unknown natural causes (Newton, Meek & Little 1986, Bibby 1986 & 1987, Meek 1988, Crick *in press*, Rebecca *et al.* 1992, Parr *in press*, Benn 1989, Heavisides 1992, Little & Davison 1992). **It is possible, however, that some of these partial and complete breeding failures may have been occasioned by the data-gathering activities of the researchers themselves. Birds already under stress due to prolonged inclement weather, inadequate shelter at the nest site and diminished and/or degraded foraging habitat, are most likely to be at risk from repeated disturbance at or near the nest.**

Since the Merlin remains " the most heavily polluted of the British raptors " (Newton & Haas 1988) and because eggshell thinning and breakage still occur in a proportion of all Scottish Merlin populations, though not at levels considered likely to cause failure of the whole clutch (Newton *et al.* 1982a, Newton & Haas 1988, Meek 1988, Ellis & Okill 1990, Rebecca *et al.* 1992), the additional stresses caused by human disturbance when birds are incubating should be avoided. The following report on a Merlin study conducted in 1988 in south-east Scotland would appear to illustrate some of the attendant risks of repeated nest monitoring : *"At least 42 sites were checked, a total of 37 were occupied. A minimum of 12 sites raised at least 36 young. One area which received the best coverage produced 19 occupied sites out of 24 checked. However, only 19 young fledged from 12 nests. Five sites failed completely at egg stage, whilst 3 produced only one young each. Eggs have been sent for pesticide analysis"* (Benn 1989).

Following unfavourable weather conditions early in the 1991 breeding season, nest contents were monitored during the incubation period in the same area : *"**Lammermuirs**. A particularly cold late spring resulted in most Merlins getting off to a late start. In one case young could not have fledged before the middle of August. On the other hand one nest was exceptionally early, eggs being laid during the third week of April! Two sites were well occupied but failed before or shortly after egg laying. Ten nests were found, but one scrape was empty when located and the site was unoccupied thereafter. Two nests failed at the small young stage and one before hatching. The early nest fledged before the young could be ringed but at least two were raised from three eggs. Only 15 young were ringed from the remaining five nests. This was the poorest level of success so far during the seven years of the study.*
***Moorfoots**. Eight sites were clearly occupied and at least six reached the egg stage. Two of these failed for uncertain reasons during incubation. In two nests four and three young respectively were ringed. Another brood of five small young were found and some at least fledged. One nest was not located but at least one young fledged from this. A "normal" occupation and success rate for this area"* (Heavisides 1992).

In 1990, licensed workers reporting to RSPB Species Protection Officers in Edinburgh and to the U.K. Joint Nature Conservation Committee (which submits species distribution data to those responsible for drafting Indicative Forest Strategies), visited 367+ Merlin territories in the Highlands and Southern Uplands of Scotland; birds were observed in 280+ territories and 207+ pairs laid; 166+ clutches hatched and 159+ pairs raised 497+ young to fledging (Benn, 1991; Galbraith & Bates 1991). These figures suggest that more than 70% of the known population of Scottish Merlins was subjected to the risks of data gathering at or near the nest in a single year.

Whilst data gathering by ornithologists can be an important and commendable activity, perhaps the establishment of undisturbed control areas for 50% of the Merlin population in each of the Scottish regions should be given serious consideration by the Scottish Natural Heritage agency, as one aspect of a long-term Merlin conservation strategy, with monitoring of nest contents in such areas to be conducted by licensees only on a regular cycle of say five or six years. *It would be fitting for the Forestry Commission, as Scotland's largest land manager, and entirely in keeping with the Commission's statutory remit to conserve "fauna of special interest", to take the lead in this direction by formally declaring the Galloway Forest Park a Merlin Refuge if not a Raptor Sanctuary.*

18. Recently fledged Merlin basks in the sun.

7   CONCLUSIONS

The following conclusions are relevant to recommendations for management of the Merlin population on and near forest lands in south-west Scotland.

7.1   MERLIN POPULATION

The Merlin population in the Galloway project area in 1987 was estimated at 20-25 pairs. **The species is, therefore, sufficiently uncommon to merit special conservation measures**. Whilst it is anticipated that some 30 to 40% of the 30+ nesting territories located from 1986-91 in recently afforested areas will eventually be abandoned due to maturing of nearby plantations and loss of open ground, the prospects for conserving a small population of Merlins in the Galloway and Carrick Hills are favourable if sufficient areas of moorland foraging habitat are preserved. Availability of moorland foraging habitat is considered to be the main long-term limiting factor.

7.2   MOORLAND CONSERVATION AND MANAGEMENT

Preservation of moorland hunting habitat and maintaining continuity of preferred forest nesting habitat close to moorland areas are the prime management needs. Since each pair of Merlins requires a substantial area of moorland foraging habitat (possibly more than 20 km^2), the task of conserving the species on ground devoted to forestry is particularly challenging. Merlins breeding within a forest may hunt over lands managed by several owners and can, therefore, be affected by land-use changes leading to deterioration or improvement of foraging habitat at considerable distances from the nest. The Forestry Commission, Scottish Natural Heritage and several private estates manage large tracts of moorland in four parts of the project area, which (if they remain largely unafforested) should continue to support a viable population of birds.

In the Galloway project area hill sheep farming is the major land use on the open ground hunted by Merlins, Hen Harriers, Buzzards and Ravens. For wildlife conservation purposes and to maintain rural communities *this form of land use must be encouraged where it prevails, especially within and adjacent to the Galloway Forest Park, particularly near existing nature reserves*. The need for retention of open ground outside designated sites has been emphasised by Ratcliffe (1986a,b) whilst Peterken (1986 & 1987) has stressed the value of retaining open-ground habitats within the forest fence to help maintain species richness. **It is important to note that the implementation of a multiple land-use policy within the Forest Park, in addition to establishing a substantial timber resource, has created habitat diversity and allowed the Merlin to maintain a significant (if somewhat diminished) presence as a breeding bird. If a similar policy were to**

be adopted by the Forestry Authority in other Scottish regions, then a "reasonable balance between the production and supply of timber and the conservation of fauna of special interest" could be achieved.

At a future date, mowing and/or controlled burning of heather may have to be considered on some Forestry Commission lands in south-west Scotland in order to create a patchwork of varied-age heather plants in moorland areas from which sheep have been removed. Appropriate moorland management should benefit populations of upland birds including gamebirds and Merlin prey species; there is no shortage of relevant advice (Reed 1985, Hudson 1984, Hudson 1986, Haworth & Fielding 1988, Felton & Marsden 1990, Lawton 1990, Brown 1991, Mitchell & Straker-Smith 1991, Phillips 1991).

7.3   MAXIMISING BREEDING PERFORMANCE

It is well known by experienced ornithologists and evident from the range of reports mentioned earlier in Section 6.5 that human disturbance of breeding Merlins may have adverse effects : 1) nest monitoring may encourage natural predation; 2) ground-nesting and tree-nesting Merlins disturbed during courtship, egg-laying and the early incubation period may desert the nest site; 3) prolonged or repeated disturbance later in the incubation period and when the eggs are hatching can result in partial or complete breeding failure, particularly if the birds are already under stress. **In order to maximise the breeding success of Merlins in the city of Saskatoon, which now has the highest recorded nesting density for this species, tree nests have not been inspected by researchers during the incubation period in recent years** (Oliphant & Haug 1985, L.W. Oliphant pers. comm.). **Incubating birds were not disturbed for the same reason during the Galloway Forests Merlin Survey.**

It would seem prudent, therefore, for forest and estate managers in Dumfries and Galloway Region and other parts of Scotland to place restrictions on potentially disruptive forestry operations and other potentially harmful activities near active nest sites. **Buffer or exclusion zones (of approximately 400 metres radius) could be established around vulnerable nests** during the breeding season as suggested for parts of N.America by Becker & Ball (1983); this could greatly improve the birds' chances of breeding successfully. **Before granting permission for nest monitoring, landowners, factors and forest managers should satisfy themselves that the conservation benefits of any proposed disturbance are likely to outweigh the potential risks to breeding Merlins.** Figure 23 indicates the sensitivity of Merlins to human activity throughout the breeding cycle.

Fig. 23. SENSITIVITY OF MERLINS TO HUMAN ACTIVITY DURING THE BREEDING SEASON

MARCH. APRIL. MAY . JUNE. JULY . AUG .

Choosing nest site

Incubating

Nestlings

Fledglings

■■■■■■■■ Most sensitive to human activity

IIIIIIIIIIIIIII Less sensitive to human activity

░░░░░░░░░░░ Least sensitive to human activity

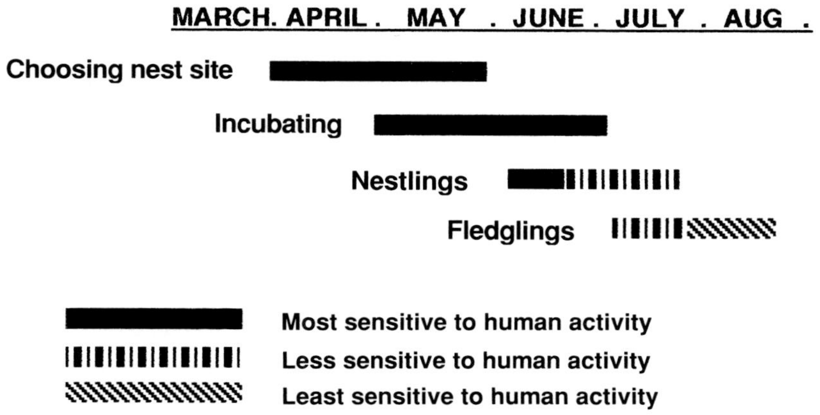

7. 4 RESEARCH REQUIREMENTS

To aid habitat and species management in Scotland, more information is required on the following aspects of Merlin ecology.

7. 4. a FORAGING BEHAVIOUR

Radio telemetry data on the Merlin's use of specific foraging habitats, in particular open spaces within the forest, could prove useful. It is important to understand how home ranges relate to topography, prey densities and vegetation of unplanted ground as well as to forest design and structure. The habitat data presented in this report were gathered from an area of 4 km fixed radius around nest sites, yet it is probable that in some cases Merlin foraging areas exceeded this range and conformed to particular elongated valley systems. Becker and Sieg (1987) have shown that male Merlins breeding on the Montana prairies routinely overfly tilled agricultural land to hunt in natural grassland habitat, and Warkentin and Oliphant (1990) have demonstrated that wintering urban Merlins have preferred foraging places within their extensive hunting ranges. It would be helpful to identify regular foraging routes and preferred hunting locations during the breeding season in a range of afforested landscapes in the Scottish uplands.

7. 4. b RELATIONSHIP WITH OTHER RAPTORS AND CORVIDS

Comprehensive data on forest raptor and corvid communities related to forest structure and foraging habitats, are required for informed management of the rarer forest raptors. *The Galloway Forests Merlin Project evolved during 1988-89 into the Forest Raptor Project,* which is providing monthly raptor data from more than 20 study areas in several mixed-age forests. It is hoped that this long-term research project will continue to demonstrate how effectively forest ranger teams can implement the Forestry Commission's objectives for nature conservation (FC 1986).

7. 4. c POPULATION ECOLOGY

Whilst it is evident that a pair of Merlins must only beget two "parents" during their lifetime to maintain population stability, relatively little is known about the age structure, mortality, recruitment and site fidelity of British Merlin populations. Fidelity to nest territories would appear to be fairly high among female Merlins in north and north-east Scotland and Wales where populations are now considered to be stable (Ellis & Okill 1990, G Rebecca pers. comm., Bibby 1986, Parr *in press*). A comparative study of 2 or 3 widely spaced groups of 15-20 pairs would provide insight into the dynamics of forest and moorland populations in Scotland. Relevant population studies in Canada, Iceland and Alaska have proved instructive. (Hodson 1976, Warkentin *et al.* 1991, Nielsen 1986, Titus & Schempf 1990). **However, in view of the already vulnerable status of the Merlin in and near the Galloway Forest Park, it would not be appropriate to include the Galloway population in any intensive study involving catching of breeding adults and increased disturbance of nesting birds.**

19. Hen with large chicks on crag ledge, Galloway 1977.

8 RECOMMENDATIONS FOR MANAGEMENT OF THE MERLIN POPULATION ON AND NEAR FOREST LANDS IN SOUTH-WEST SCOTLAND.

8.1 SAFEGUARDING PRIME MOORLAND FORAGING AREAS

The Galloway Forests Merlin Project of 1986-89 and Forest Raptor Project which began in 1988/9 have demonstrated that in the south-west Scotland project area Merlins generally nest in coniferous plantations close to large moorland areas which provide much of their prey. Between 1987 and 1991 some of the moorlands which were identified during the 1986-87 survey (Orchel and Livingstone 1988) as prime foraging habitat for Merlins were subject to further partial or extensive afforestation. **In order to maintain the Merlin population in the Galloway project area at about 20 pairs, it is recommended that the remaining network of semi-natural moorland foraging areas (particularly within and near the Galloway Forest Park, in the Glenkens and in the western watersheds) is conserved and managed sympathetically,**

The establishment of the Stewartry Environmentally Sensitive Area (DAFS 1989) was a firsty step in this direction and the proposed Western Southern Uplands ESA, should provide financial support for positive management of most of the remaining, semi-natural moorland areas within the project area (Scottish Office 1992, Appendix 9). *Applications for grant aid for new planting within the existing and proposed ESA (see FC 1991d) will need to be considered with the utmost care by the Forestry Authority to ensure that they comply with the Environmental Assessment (Afforestation) Regulations 1988 (SI 1988/1207) and do not lead to a significant reduction of the remaining moorland network and displacement of Merlins from preferred breeding areas.*

8. 2   EXTENDING FORAGING AREAS THROUGH IMPROVED FOREST DESIGN

Merlins are able to survive in areas which are moderately afforested, yet only where 1) large tracts of unbroken moorland separate existing forests and 2) substantial enclaves of low-lying and higher altitude grass and heather moorland are incorporated into the forest design to create an extensive patchwork of open ground and associated forest edge foraging habitats within 4 to 5 km of nesting areas (e.g. Figure 21). At the felling and restocking stage the opportunity should be taken to extend these foraging areas.

To extend open ground and forest edge foraging habitats for Merlins it is recommended that forest managers -

a) establish a network of wide, sparsely treed, riparian zones of varying breadth along watercourses throughout the forest in which occasional groups of broadleaved trees and shrubs should be planted to diversify habitat and attract small birds; small headwater corridors (as shown in Photo 10) should be *more than 5 m wide on each bank,* whereas larger streams and rivers require a corridor *two or three times as wide as the stream bed on each bank;* *
b) increase and vary the width of open habitats along other permanent corridors (roads and power lines) by indenting compartment edges and planting groups of broadleaved trees and shrubs;
c) ensure that all major farmland, wetland and moorland enclaves are linked by permanent wildlife corridors (50 to 100+ metres in width) including redesigned forest rides and fire-breaks which harmoniously reflect landform;
d) refrain from replanting areas of low yield and where timber extraction has been difficult;
e) create a patchwork of varied-age felling coupes which are asymmetrical and irregular, shaped to follow landform and are of reasonable size at higher elevations (e.g. > 100 ha above 250 m);
f) make upper forest margins irregular and reshape straight lateral edges into gently curving, windfirm diagonals, all of which should reflect the quality of landform.

Note. Reference should be made to *"Forest Landscape Design Guidelines"* (FC 1989), the *"Guide to Upland Restocking Practice"* (FC 1985) and *"Forests and Water Guidelines"* (FC 1991) for more detailed advice on restructuring. Information about suitable native trees and shrubs matched to geographic zones (Soutar & Peterken 1989) is presented in *"Forest Nature Conservation Guidelines"* (FC 1990).
* See page 13 of *"Forests and Water Guidelines"*.

8.3   MANAGEMENT OF NESTING AREAS

It is vital that preferred nesting areas are identified and provision is made to maintain continuity of 1) forest nesting habitat close to moorland foraging areas and 2) ground nesting cover on moorland enclaves.

a) At the felling stage a variety of stands of mature conifers (ranging from 1 to 5+ ha, in scale with the landscape) need to be retained on windfirm sites close to moorland foraging areas to provide Merlins with a selection of suitable nest sites in trees within and near preferred nesting territories;
b) small mixed copses of native broadleaves and conifers (1 to 5+ ha, in harmony with the landscape) should be planted at wide spacing for long-term retention at intervals of 0.5 to 1.0 km along forest-moorland boundaries to provide permanent nesting places;
c) where existing constraints and agreements permit, small copses of native broadleaves should be established hamoniously in remote areas of the Galloway Forest Park to restore habitat diversity and provide permanent and secure nesting sites on open land;
d) heather should be managed to provide nesting cover for Merlins (also Hen Harriers, Short-eared Owls and gamebirds) in preferred breeding areas above the timberline and on extensive moorland enclaves : large patches of deep heather (30-50 cm in height and > 2 ha) should be maintained;
e) trees should be cleared from slopes below some traditional nesting crags within 500 metres of large moors to encourage re-occupation;

20. Hen guards crag nest from top of nearby larch, Galloway 1977.

8.4 REDUCING DISTURBANCE

The Merlin is listed on Schedule 1 of the Wildlife and Countryside Act 1981 and is protected at all times of the year. The Act prohibits intentional disturbance by unlicensed persons whilst Merlins are establishing a nest site, or are in, on or near a nest containing eggs or young. It is also illegal to intentionally disturb dependent young which have left the nest.

a) *Forest managers* **need to ensure that any disturbance in the breeding season (from early April to early August) is by workers licensed by Scottish Natural Heritage and that nest visits are justified on scientific *and* conservation grounds.**

To maximise breeding success, licensees should be asked to observe forest and moorland nesting areas in April, May and early June *from a safe distance* (preferably > 400 m from the nest), which will allow confirmation of tenancy, and to conduct nest inspections to obtain breeding data *at a sample of sites,* only when frequent prey deliveries indicate that there are young in the nest (generally after 20th June).

b) *Forest rangers* employed by the Forestry Commission and private forestry companies in South Scotland Conservancy have developed considerable expertise in raptor survey work and **should be encouraged to continue to record the presence of active Merlin nesting territories on their beats, concentrating on compartments which have been scheduled for thinning and clearfelling within 500 m of open moorland and large moorland enclaves.** Relevant information about nesting birds should be reported to the responsible forest manager who should request nest site inspection by a **licensed Conservation Ranger** and, if necessary, take steps to curtail forestry operations and other activities likely to cause disturbance within known nesting areas, especially within 400 m of known nest sites during the breeding season.

8.5 PREDATOR CONTROL

Control of Foxes and Carrion Crows should only be undertaken where it is likely to prove beneficial and cost-effective i.e. primarily in plantations adjacent to nature reserves and Sites of Special Scientific Interest which already provide or have the potential to provide habitat for significant populations of moorland birds. To protect ground-nesting birds without diminishing the supply of nest sites in conifers for small falcons, **Crows should only be controlled after nest building,** preferably in April and May. It is recommended that Larsen-type cage traps are employed for this purpose.

GENERAL MERLIN CONSERVATION GUIDELINES FOR FOREST AND ESTATE MANAGERS IN SCOTLAND

Through their silvicultural practices and management of extensive tracts of unplanted land (mainly farmland and moorland) the state and private forestry sectors in Scotland already maintain and enhance a wide range of habitats for birds of prey. For example, in 1989-90 the area of unplanted land (potential, non-woodland, foraging habitat for raptors and owls) managed by the Forestry Commission in Scotland was 180,234 ha or 24.9% of the entire FC estate of 723,497 ha (Forestry Commission 1991a). Private woodlands in Scotland covered more than 587,000 ha in the same year (Forestry Commission 1991b).

Today, within the broad context of Regional Structure Plans which include Indicative Forest Strategies, new forestry grants provide support to the private forestry sector for managing and improving the design of existing plantations and for the establishment of new forests that meet the FC Environment Guidelines for nature conservation, water protection and landscape design. The following Merlin conservation guidelines are, therefore, presented in four sections, three of which relate to major stages in the forest cycle whilst the fourth applies to management of moorland nesting and foraging areas.

21. Vigilant falcon in larch.

9. 1 CONSERVATION IN NEW PLANTATIONS

Long-term conservation goals can be achieved primarily through the creation of sensitive forest designs which provide sufficient, open ground, foraging habitat beyond and within the forest fence to maintain breeding Merlins through the entire forest cycle, not merely the ephemeral, prey-rich establishment phase. In pre-thicket and early thicket-stage plantations Merlins are likely to nest on the ground in heather (and occasionally bracken) or on a vegetated crag ledge. Occupation of traditional ground-nesting sites within plantations can last from 5 to 20+ years following afforestation, depending on the proximity and availability of moorland hunting areas.

To conserve the Merlin it is recommended that forest managers -

a) leave extensive areas of open moorland foraging habitat above the timberline and between major forest complexes within each watershed;

b) leave large patches of deep heather (30 to 50 cm high and > 2.0 ha) on traditional nesting slopes to encourage continuity of use until corvid nests become available at the forest edge;

c) leave slopes below potential nesting crags unplanted;

d) plant mixed copses of native broadleaves and conifers* (1 to 5+ ha, in harmony with the landscape and at wide spacing for long-term retention) at intervals of 0.5 to 1.0 km along forest-moorland boundaries to create permanent nesting places;

e) **create an extensive network of wide riparian corridors with associated irregular forest edges to act as permanent raptor foraging areas within the forest** (see 8. 2 above);

f) ensure that other permanent open spaces (roads, rides, fire-breaks, farmland, wetland, unplantable ground) are fully integrated within a forest design which reflects landform and that important wildlife corridors are of appropriate width (50 to 100+ metres);

g) ensure that top margins reflect landform and provide irregular forest edge foraging areas;

h) request wildlife managers to identify and monitor active nesting areas from a safe distance (preferably > 400 m);

i) **minimise human disturbance near active nesting areas during the breeding season;**

* Mixed copses can benefit many other species including Black Grouse *Tetrao tetrix;* see 9.4.

9. 2   CONSERVATION IN HIGH FOREST

Following canopy closure, Merlins usually nest in trees close to the forest edge, although ground nesting may sometimes occur on moorland enclaves within closed-canopy plantations where extensive moorland foraging areas remain.

To conserve the Merlin forest managers should -

a) have active forest nesting areas identified early in the breeding season (April/May), concentrating survey efforts on compartments scheduled for thinning, situated within 0.5 km of forest-moorland boundaries;
b) **defer plans to thin trees within 400 m radius of occupied nest sites;**
c) **minimise human disturbance near occupied nesting places during the breeding season.**
d) ensure that, where predator control is practised in compartments adjacent to moorland, incubating Merlins are not accidentally shot off corvid nests (see Section 8.5).

22. Hen Merlin with young brood in abandoned crow nest. Small chicks depend on her for food, shelter and nest defence. *(Photo : Roy Blewitt)*

9.3   CONSERVATION AT CLEARFELLING AND REPLANTING

At this stage Merlins are likely to continue nesting in mature conifers, though ground or crag nesting within or above the forest may occasionally occur. Harvesting operations pose a potential threat to breeding birds as nesting areas may be disturbed and stands containing active nests may be accidentally felled.

To conserve the Merlin it is recommended that forest managers -

a) ensure that wildlife managers identify occupied nesting areas early in the breeding season (April/May), concentrating survey efforts on compartments scheduled for clearfelling;

b) **ensure that trees within 400m radius of active nest sites are not felled during the breeding season;**

c) **retain a variety of stands of overmature trees (from 1 to 5+ ha, in harmony with the landscape) on windfirm sites close to moorland to encourage continuity of tree nesting in and near known nesting territories;**

d) where appropriate, plant additional mixed copses of widely spaced native broadleaves and conifers (1 to 5+ ha, in scale with the landscape) at intervals of 0.5 to 1.0 km along forest-moorland boundaries to create permanent nesting places;

e) extend open space for foraging within the forest by not replanting areas of low yield or where timber extraction has been difficult; *

f) **where appropriate, modify the existing system of rides and riparian corridors within the forest (as described in Section 8. 3) to create additional open ground foraging habitat;**

g) extend forest edge and open ground foraging areas by creating felling coupes of varied ages, which are asymmetrical and irregular, shaped to follow landform and at higher elevations are of reasonable size (e.g. > 100 ha above 250 m);

h) **minimise human disturbance in active nesting areas;**

*See page 9 of " *Guide to Upland Restocking Practice*" (FC 1985).

9. 4 CONSERVATION ON MOORLAND

The primary objective should be to maintain moorland vegetation in a vigorous condition by appropriate means (e.g. limited grazing, controlled burning, mowing) to provide a variety of breeding and foraging habitats for moorland birds. Merlins may nest in deep heather, bracken or in a moorland tree. Moderate to steep heather-clad slopes, near the headwaters of moorland streams are favoured nesting places (Williams 1981, Rebecca & ` Payne 1985, Haworth & Fielding 1988).

To conserve the Merlin it is recommended that forest and estate managers -

a) **restore overgrazed heather by excluding or regulating numbers of sheep, cattle and deer in order to improve nesting cover for moorland birds; thereafter maintain habitat diversity via a long-term moorland management plan;**
b) retain and where possible expand insect-rich bogs and damp flushes as wetland breeding and foraging areas for ground-nesting birds;
c) **retain large patches of deep heather** (30 to 50 cm high and > 2 ha) **in traditional Merlin nesting areas;**
d) plant small copses of native broadleaves and/or native pine* along sheltered parts of moorland watercourses to diversify habitat and provide permanent nesting places;
e) restore semi-natural woodland** along moorland watercourses by fencing off in order to establish permanent nesting sites;
f) make sure that, where predator control is practised to protect assemblages of nesting moorland birds, corvids (Carrion/Hooded Crows and Magpies) are controlled after nest building and without risk to breeding Merlins (see Section 8.5 and 9.2d);
g) site artificial nesting platforms in remote moorland trees and copses where corvid nests may be lacking (see Appendix 4);
h) have occupied sites identified from a safe distance (> 400 m);
i) **ensure that human disturbance near occupied nesting areas is minimised.**

Note. Small, mixed copses of widely spaced trees sited at irregular intervals (> 500 m) can provide winter shelter and spring feed for Black Grouse when planted on and near large blocks of heather moorland (e.g. 500 to 1000 ha). Important species are larch, Scots pine, birch, hazel and rowan. (Picozzi & Catt 1988).

*   Grants are available from the Forestry Authority for the establishment of new native pinewoods.
** Grants to encourage natural regeneration and special management grants for maintaining and improving woodlands of high environmental value are also available.

23.
An upland valley hunted
by Galloway Merlins.
Five thousand years ago
deciduous woodland
covered most of this ground.
Today tracts of high moorland,
coniferous forest glades
and meadows provide
avian prey for Merlins and
other breeding raptors.
A balance between
semi-natural moorland,
farmland and afforested
ground must be maintained
throughout Scotland's
watersheds to conserve
populations of native birds.

24.
Raptor watch in the Galloway
Forest Park,1986. The Galloway
Forests Merlin Project encouraged
forest rangers to identify nesting
areas of rare birds to aid habitat
and species management. Nests
were watched from a distance
and breeding birds were not
disturbed.

10 SPECIAL RECOMMENDATION :
SUPPORT FOR NATURE CONSERVATION IN PRIVATE WOODLANDS

This report presents evidence of the role of commercial woodlands as refuges for rare and vulnerable birds of prey and highlights the important contribution made by forest rangers in gathering data to promote management of habitats for "fauna of special interest".

The Hawk and Owl Trust, therefore, welcomes the recent introduction of forest management grants yet strongly recommends to the Forestry Commission that the incentives for management of wildlife habitats be reviewed and increased. Of particular benefit would be the introduction of a system of grants to forest management companies (in charge of more than 10,000 ha of afforested ground in Scotland) *to encourage and support increased employment of forest rangers responsible for crop protection and conservation of rare and vulnerable species.*

Sensitive avian species breeding on afforested lands include Merlin, Golden Eagle, Hen Harrier, Barn Owl, Goshawk, Osprey, Peregrine and Short-eared Owl, which are listed in Annex 1 of the EC Wild Birds Directive 1979 requiring EC member states to take special measures to protect them; all but the last appear on Schedule 1 of the Wildlife and Countryside Act 1981 which affords them the highest level of protection under British law. **Since the area of private woodland in Scotland now exceeds 600,000 ha (6,000 km^2) and is growing steadily by about 11,000 ha per annum (FC 1992) there is clearly room for employment of greater numbers of full-time wildlife specialists in the private forestry sector. At present their number falls well below the complement of 131 forest rangers on the Forestry Commission's payroll in Scotland and is reducing rather than increasing.**

11 APPENDICES

APPENDIX 1 SCIENTIFIC NAMES OF PLANTS AND ANIMALS

Plants

Alder	*Alnus* spp.
Ash	*Fraxinus excelsior*
Bents	*Agrostis* spp.
Bilberry	*Vaccinium myrtillus*
Birch	*Betula* spp.
Bog-moss	*Sphagnum* spp.
Bog myrtle	*Myrica gale*
Bracken	*Pteridium aquilinum*
Cotton-grass	*Eriophorum* spp.
Deer-grass	*Trichophorum caespitosum*
Elm	*Ulmus* spp.
Flying bent (Purple moor-grass)	*Molinia caerulea*
Hawthorn	*Crataegus monogyna*
Hazel	*Corylus avellana*
Heather : Ling	*Calluna vulgaris*
Bell heather	*Erica cinerea*
Cross-leaved heath	*Erica tetralix*
Heath rush	*Juncus squarrosus*
Juniper	*Juniperus* spp.
Larch	*Larix* spp.
Matt-grass	*Nardus stricta*
Oak	*Quercus* spp.
Poplar	*Populus* spp.
Pine :	*Pinus* spp.
Lodgepole pine	*Pinus contorta*
Scots pine	*Pinus sylvestris*
Rowan	*Sorbus aucuparia*
Sedge	*Carex* spp.
Sheep's fescue	*Festuca ovina*
Spruce :	*Picea* spp.
Norway spruce	*Picea abies*
Sitka spruce	*Picea sitchensis*
Sweet vernal-grass	*Anthoxanthum odoratum*
Wavy hair-grass	*Deschampsia flexuosa*
Willow	*Salix* spp.

Birds

American Crow	*Corvus brachyrhynchos*
Barn Owl	*Tyto alba*
Blackbird	*Turdus merula*
Black Grouse	*Tetrao tetrix*
Bullfinch	*Pyrrhula pyrrhula*
Buzzard	*Buteo buteo*
Carrion Crow	*Corvus corone*
Chaffinch	*Fringilla coelebs*
Crossbill	*Loxia curvirostra*
Cuckoo	*Cuculus canorus*
Dunlin	*Calidris alpina*
Goldcrest	*Regulus regulus*
Golden Eagle	*Aquila chrysaetos*
Golden Plover	*Pluvialis apricaria*
Goshawk	*Accipiter gentilis*
Gyrfalcon	*Falco rusticolus*
Hen Harrier	*Circus cyaneus*
Hobby	*Falco subbuteo*
Hooded Crow	*Corvus corone cornix*
House Martin	*Delichon urbica*

House Sparrow	*Passer domesticus*
Kestrel	*Falco tinnunculus*
Linnet	*Carduelis cannabina*
Long-eared Owl	*Asio otus*
Magpie	*Pica pica*
Meadow Pipit	*Anthus pratensis*
Merlin :	*Falco columbarius* Linnaeus
European Merlin	*Falco c. aesalon* Tunstall
Icelandic Merlin	*Falco c. subaesalon* Brehm
North American Merlin of taiga	*Falco c. columbarius* Linnaeus
Richardson's Merlin	*Falco c. richardsonii* Ridgway
Mistle Thrush	*Turdus viscivorus*
Osprey	*Pandion haliaetus*
Peregrine	*Falco peregrinus*
Pied wagtail	*Motacilla alba*
Raven	*Corvus corax*
Red Grouse	*Logopus lagopus*
Red Kite	*Milvus milvus*
Redshank	*Tringa totanus*
Rock Pipit	*Anthus spinoletta*
Rough-legged Buzzard	*Buteo lagopus*
Short-eared Owl	*Asiuo flammeus*
Siskin	*Carduelis spinus*
Skylark	*Alauda arvensis*
Snipe	*Gallinago gallinago*
Sparrowhawk	*Accipiter nisus*
Starling	*Sturnus vulgaris*
Stonechat	*Saxicola torquata*
Swallow	*Hirundo rustica*
Tawny Owl	*Strix aluco*
Wheatear	*Oenanthe oenanthe*
Willow Warbler	*Phylloscopus trochilus*

Insects

Dragonfly	*Odonata*
Emperor Moth	*Pavonia pavonia*
Fox Moth	*Macrothylacia rubi*
Ground beetle	*Carabidae*
Northern Eggar Moth	*Lasiocampa quercus callunae*

Mammals

Fox	*Vulpes vulpes*
Short-tailed Field Vole	*Microtus agrestis*
Red Deer	*Cervus elaphus*
Roe Deer	*Capreolus capreolus*

Fish

Atlantic Salmon	Salmo salar

Foraging areas available within 4 km radius (50.2 km²) of Merlin nest sites (n = 20) in south-west Scotland, 1986-87.

Nest	Nest site type	Grass moorland	Improved grassland	Heather moorland	Arable land	Scrub	Young conifer forest (1-7 years)	Restocked conifer forest (1-7 years)	Forest glades (rides etc)	Mature forest edge	Forest roads	Hedgerows	Broadleaved woodland	Well-grown conifer forest. (8-50+ years)
a	b	c	d	e	f	g	h	i	j	k	l	m	n	o
		km²	km²	km²	km²	km²	km²	km²	km²	km	km	km	km²	km²
1	C	11.2	-	22.10	-	-	-	-	0.7	23.0	18.0	-	-	14.1
2	C	15.7	1.80	2.60	0.22	0.35	10.70	0.06	1.4	22.0	25.0	c0.50	0.30	16.8
3	C	17.4	0.20	2.50	0.02	0.04	17.00	-	1.5	31.0	24.0	<1.00	0.03	11.4
4	C	6.2	0.10	0.60	-	0.03	11.80	-	2.1	23.0	35.0	<1.00	0.02	28.8
5	C	33.2	0.50	0.10	0.06	0.33	0.10	-	0.8	32.0	14.0	-	0.02	15.1
6	C	34.0	0.60	1.30	0.06	0.33	0.50	-	0.7	22.0	17.0	-	0.02	12.7
7	C	11.4	-	2.20	-	0.01	1.10	-	1.8	38.0	37.0	-	-	33.7
8	C	17.0	0.10	8.10	-	0.01	-	-	1.2	33.0	26.0	<1.00	0.02	23.6
9	C	26.2	2.00	1.40	0.10	0.51	-	0.60	0.9	26.0	29.0	c0.50	0.72	16.8
10	C	14.8	3.20	10.60	0.12	0.38	6.50	0.06	1.0	25.0	16.0	c0.10	0.56	13.0
11	C	22.9	0.60	7.00	0.04	0.11	9.10	-	1.0	39.0	18.0	c0.50	0.21	9.0
12	C	26.1	0.05	1.70	-	0.01	-	-	1.1	37.0	36.0	-	0.01	21.2
13	C	25.8	0.70	7.90	0.05	0.15	-	-	0.5	37.0	7.0	c0.50	0.53	9.1
14	C	4.9	-	16.50	-	-	-	0.80	1.1	26.0	37.0	-	-	20.6
15	C	18.7	2.40	5.00	0.07	0.23	7.20	0.30	1.2	22.0	33.0	c0.60	0.15	14.5
16	C	18.5	0.08	8.20	0.01	-	-	0.80	1.2	43.0	29.0	<1.00	-	21.4
17	B	15.5	1.50	11.20	0.25	0.31	3.80	2.50	1.0	44.0	41.0	c0.40	0.85	13.1
18	H	25.0	0.90	13.10	0.10	0.02	5.20	-	0.5	17.0	7.0	c0.20	0.11	5.2
19	H	15.0	-	17.20	-	-	0.60	-	0.8	31.0	12.0	-	-	15.6
20	H	27.3	1.30	6.90	0.18	0.10	9.00	-	0.7	15.0	11.0	c0.20	0.9	4.5

C = nest in conifer; B = stick nest in broadleaved tree; H = ground nest in heather.

Nests 1-17 in conifer plantations; nests 18-20 on moorland.

APPENDIX 3

Summary of bird of prey and corvid surveys of recently restocked forest sites (1-7 years) in south-west Scotland, 1986-87.

	1986 Study areas							Total areas where seen		1987 Study areas											Total areas where seen	
Area No. :	6	7	16	18	21	23	24	No.	%	6	7	10	16	18	19	21	22	23	24	31	No.	%
SPECIES																						
1. Kestrel**	P	P	P	P	P	P	P	7	100	P	P	P	P	P	P	P	P	P	P	P	11	100
2. Short-eared Owl*	-	-	-	-	P	-	P	2	28	-	-	-	-	P	P	-	P	P	P	-	5	45
3. Barn Owl**	-	-	-	-	P	-	-	1	14	-	-	P	-	-	-	P	-	-	-	-	2	18
4. Sparrowhawk**	P	P	-	P	P	-	P	5	71	P	P	P	-	-	P	P	P	P	P	P	9	81
5. Buzzard**	P	P	P	P	P	P	P	7	100	P	P	-	P	P	P	P	P	P	P	P	10	91
6. Hen Harrier	-	-	P	-	-	-	-	1	14	P	-	-	-	P	-	-	P	P	-	-	4	36
7. Merlin	-	-	-	-	-	-	-	0	0	-	-	P	P	-	-	-	-	-	-	-	2	18
8. Peregrine	-	-	P	-	P	-	-	2	28	-	-	-	P	-	-	-	-	-	-	?	1	9
9. Goshawk	-	-	-	-	-	-	-	0	0	-	-	-	-	-	-	P	-	-	-	-	1	9
10. Carrion Crow**	P	P	P	P	P	P	P	7	100	P	P	P	P	P	P	P	P	P	P	P	11	100
11. Raven**	P	-	P	-	P	-	-	3	42	P	-	P	P	P	-	P	-	-	P	-	6	54
12. Magpie**	P	-	-	-	-	-	P	2	28	P	-	-	-	-	-	-	-	-	P	-	2	18
13. Cuckoo	P	-	P	P	P	P	P	6	85	P	P	-	P	P	P	-	P	P	P	-	8	72
Species total	7	4	7	6	8	5	6			8	5	6	7	7	6	7	7	7	8	4		
Size of study area (ha)	290	150	120	215	265	90	165			290	150	65	120	215	25	265	160	90	165	155		

P = present in study area during breeding season; seen hunting.
* = nesting on ground.
** = nesting in trees next to restocked ground; Barn Owls nesting in artificial sites.
Other species seen 1988-90 : Golden Eagle (winter), Osprey (during breeding season), Red Kite (autumn).

APPENDIX 4

NESTING PLATFORM FOR MERLINS

CONSTRUCTION

a) Make a cone or basket from 1.0" (25 mm) wire netting (chicken wire) : about 14" (35 cm) in diameter x 6-7" (15-18 cm) deep. Alternatively, purchase a plastic-coated, hanging flower basket of similar dimensions. (Possible source : Bakaware Ltd., Cecil Street, Birmingham, B19 3SY)

b) Find a suitable Y fork in a moorland tree (birch / alder / rowan) with branches angled 70-90 º.

c) Tie the basket in place with plastic-coated wire or nylon rope as shown below.

d) Fill the basket with turves to within 2" (5 cm) of the top.

e) Weave twigs / heather stems through remaining netting to form a rim about 2" (5 cm) high. If using wire netting, neatly fold over surplus. Note : incubating Merlins tend to nibble twigs.

f) Add a thin piece of turf and form a cup in the basket.

25. Brood of Merlins in man-made nest.
(Photo : Graham Rebecca)

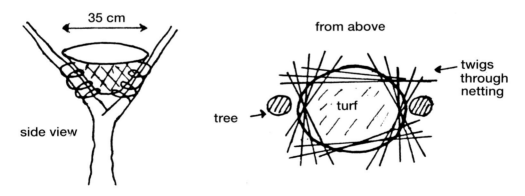

SITING

a) Site platforms in scattered trees on moorland slopes where, until recently, Merlins had used abandoned corvid nests.
b) Site platforms in groups of 2 or 3, fairly close together (< 100 m apart), depending on suitability of trees.
c) The distance between groups of platforms should be 3 to 4 km.

APPENDIX 5. Page 1 of the Merlin survey booklet prepared by the author.

Merlin Survey : Galloway Forests

About the Merlin

The Merlin, Britain's smallest falcon, breeds in the uplands from April to July. The female with her dark brown back and barred tail is larger than the male which has a blue-grey back and tail. Both sexes hunt over open country and catch small ground-nesting birds such as Meadow Pipits and small woodland species which feed at the forest edge.

On deforested moorland Merlins usually nest on the ground in deep heather or in abandoned crow nests built in solitary trees or copses. Elsewhere, Merlins are associated with blanket bogs, large clearings within forests and forest edge sites above and below timberline. Here they may nest in patches of rank heather or occupy old stick nests made by Magpies, Sparrowhawks and Crows in stands of mature conifers.

Little is known about the long-term response of Merlins to rapid afforestation of Britain's uplands. There is some evidence that the species is beginning to exploit new foraging and nesting opportunities provided by commercial forestry plantations.

About the survey

The purpose of this study is twofold: firstly to evaluate the significance of commercial forests for Merlins over a large area during the breeding season; and secondly to record the species' association with other birds of prey and members of the crow family, present on and near forestry land.

Your help is required to make this a success

APPENDIX 6. Page 2 of the Merlin survey booklet.

CODE for use on map

MERLIN	M	PEREGRINE	P
KESTREL	K	SPARROWHAWK	S
SHORT-EARED OWL	SEO	CUCKOO	CK
HEN HARRIER	HH	MAGPIE	MG
BUZZARD	B	GOSHAWK	GH
CROW	CR	GOLDEN EAGLE	GE
RAVEN	R	BARN OWL	BO

How to record sightings on map

K/10.5.86 (AM) ✗   ✗ M/11.6.86 (PM)

FACTS TO REMEMBER

1. The Merlin has been given special protection by The Wildlife and Countryside Act 1981. Merlin nests may only be visited by individuals licensed by the Nature Conservancy Council.

2. Merlins are uncommon; the jack may be confused with the male Sparrowhawk and Cuckoo. Note: jack has very pointed wings and flies with rapid wing beats.

3. Male and female like perching upright on boulders, stone walls and fence posts. Both are most likely to be seen and heard during the courtship period in April on newly planted ground or in late June/early July when feeding young.

4. Female and juvenile food begging call: slow "eep eep eep eep". Female's alarm call near nest: rapid "eek eek eek eek".

5. Merlins commonly attack Crows and large raptors which overfly their nest site. Watch Crows flying over your study area: they may be pursued by a Merlin.

HOW YOU CAN HELP

1. On each record sheet please note all raptor and corvid sightings in your study area on at least ONE day of every week from April through July. If you are not certain about the identification of a bird of prey, place a question mark ? in the appropriate box.

2. On the map provided for each fortnight's observations please note all raptor and corvid sightings in your study area to correspond with 1 above. Place an X on the map with the appropriate code letter for the species, plus date (am/pm).

3. MOST IMPORTANT: on every occasion that a Merlin is observed, enter data on record sheet and map.

4. Record information about Merlins seen outside your study area on the final page. NIL RETURNS ARE REQUIRED

Please return completed folder by August 6th latest to:

    Mr J Livingstone
    Forestry Commission
    Creebridge
    NEWTON STEWART
    DG8 6AJ

    (Tel: 0671 2420)

MANY THANKS FOR YOUR CO-OPERATION

APPENDIX 7. Typical data capture sheet from a survey booklet.

Year: 1986

Name of Recorder: D. McPHAIL

Name of Study Area: BLACK|WHITE CHALLENGE

Map Ref:

Month	Date	1		2		3		4		5		6		7		8		9		10		11		12		13		14		15		Known to be nesting (Yes/No/unsure)
MAY	AM/PM	AM	PM	AM	PM	AM	PM	AM	PM	AM	PM	AM	PM	AM	PM	AM	PM	AM	PM	AM	PM	AM	PM	AM	PM	AM	PM	AM	PM	AM	PM	

ENTER BELOW NUMBER OF BIRDS SEEN

Species														7										13					Known to be nesting
Merlin																								1					UNSURE
Kestrel	1												1											3					YES
Short-eared Owl	2																							2					YES
Hen Harrier																													
Buzzard																													
Crow	8												4											7					YES
Raven																													
Peregrine																													
Sparrowhawk	1												1																UNSURE
Cuckoo															1														?
Magpie																													

MAIN HABITAT TYPE ✓

A. Establishment Plantation ☑
B. Restocked Clearfell ☐
C. Heather/Grass Moor ☐
D. Sheepwalk ☐
E. Other (please describe) ☐

MERLIN NEST

A. In Heather
B. In Conifer
C. In Hardwood
D. On Crag/
   Cliff Ledge
E. Other (please describe)

HUMAN ACTIVITY IN STUDY AREA ✓

A. Harvesting ☐☐☐
B. Planting ☑
C. Other ☐☐☐
D. Minimal ☐☐

REMARKS (other raptors seen; raptor behaviour; weather, etc, with dates; continue overleaf.)

Merlin seen on forest ....
eating prey ....
....
....

108

APPENDIX 8

Typical map from a survey booklet showing locations of birds of prey and corvids sighted in a study area of mixed-age forest and recently afforested moorland on 1st, 7th and 13th May 1986, as recorded in Appendix 7.

KEY : CR = Carrion Crow; CK = Cuckoo; K = Kestrel; M = Merlin; SEO = Short-eared Owl; S = Sparrowhawk.

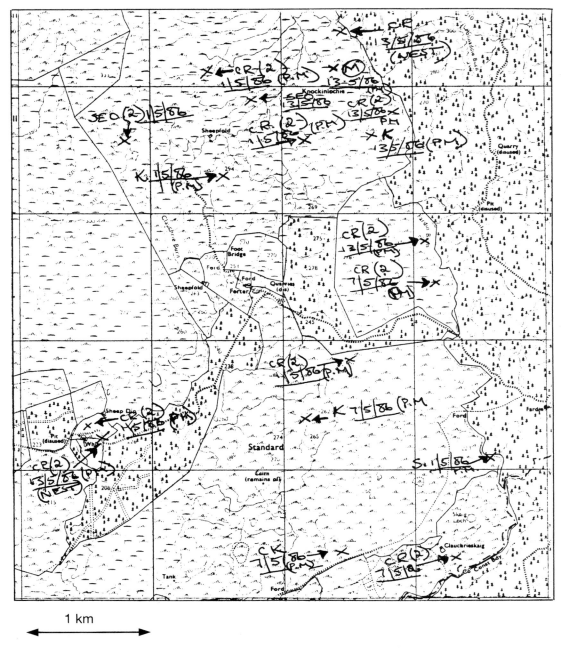

1 km

Reproduced from the 1980 Ordnance Survey 1:25000 map with the permission of the Controller of Her Majesty's Stationery Office. © Crown copyright.

APPENDIX 9   ENVIRONMENTALLY SENSITIVE AREAS IN SCOTLAND

The ESA scheme is targetted on special areas of high conservation value and provides incentives to farmers and, where relevant, crofters to protect and enhance environmental features on their land (DAFS 1989). The existing and proposed ESAs shown below encourage positive management of heather moorland and species-rich grassland. ESAs are, therefore, an important mechanism for conserving open-country foraging habitats for Merlin populations in Scotland. About 15 per cent of the total land area of Scotland is to be included in an Environmentally Sensitive Area by the end of 1993 (Scottish Office 1992).

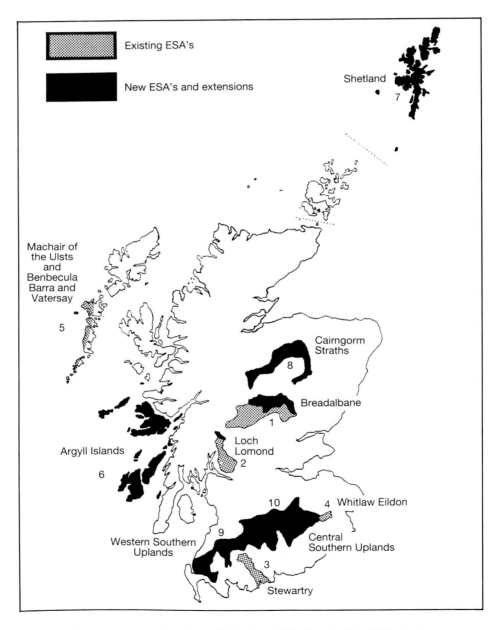

Date of ESA designation : areas 1 & 2 established in 1987; 3, 4 & 5 in 1988; 6-10 and extensions to areas 1 and 2 in 1992-93.

12   REFERENCES

1   **Anderson, M. L.** 1967. A History of Scottish Forestry : Vol. 1 & 2. (Edited by C. J. Taylor). Nelson, London.

2   **Armitage, J.** 1932. Merlin taking young from nests. British Birds, 25 : 303-304.

3   **Avery, M. and Leslie, R**. 1990. Birds and Forestry. Poyser, London.

4   **Avery, M. I., Winder, F .L. R. and Egan, V. M.** 1989. Predation on artificial nests adjacent to forestry plantations in northern Scotland. Oikos, 55 : 321-323.

5   **Batten, L. A., Bibby, C. J., Clement, P., Elliot, G. D. and Porter, R. F.** 1990. Red Data Birds in Britain. Poyser, London.

6   **Becker, D. M. and Ball, I. J.** 1983. Merlin (Falco columbarius). In : Impacts of coal surface mining on 25 migratory bird species of high Federal interest : 124-137. Edited by J. S. Armbruster. Fish and Wildlife Service, U.S. Department of the Interior, Washington, DC.

7   **Becker, D. M. and Sieg, C. H**. 1987. Home range and habitat utilization of breeding male Merlins, *Falco columbarius,* in southeastern Montana. Canadian Field-Naturalist, 101 (3) : 398-403.

8   **Beebe, F. L**. 1974. Field Studies of the Falconiformes of British Columbia. British Columbia Provincial Museum Occasional Paper Series, No.17. Victoria.

9   **Bengtson, S. A**. 1975. Hunting methods and prey of an Icelandic population of Merlin (*Falco columbarius*). Fauna och Flora, 70 : 8-12.

10   **Benn, S.** 1989. Raptor Round Up, 1988. Scottish Bird News, No. 14 : 7.

11   **Benn, S.** 1991. Raptor Round Up, 1990. Scottish Bird News, No. 22 : 8-10

12   **Bent, A. C**. 1938. Life Histories of North American Birds of Prey : Vol. 2. U.S. National Museum Bulletin 170 : 70-90. Washington, D.C. (Reprinted by Dover Publications, New York, 1961.)

13   **Bibby, C. J.** 1986. Merlins in Wales : site occupancy and breeding in relation to vegetation. Journal of Applied Ecology, 23 : 1-12.

14   **Bibby, C. J.** 1987. Foods of breeding Merlins (*Falco columbarius*) in Wales. Bird Study, 34 (1) : 64-70.

15   **Bibby, C. J. and Nattrass, M.** 1986. Breeding status of the Merlin in Britain. British Birds, 79 (4) : 170-185.

16   **Bibby, C. J., Phillips, B. N. and Seddon, A. J. E.** 1985. Birds of restocked conifer plantations in Wales. Journal of Applied Ecology, 22 : 619-633.

17   **Birks, H. H.** 1972. Studies in the vegetational history of Scotland 2 : Two pollen diagrams from the Galloway Hills, Kirkcudbrightshire. Journal of Ecology, 60 : 183-217.

18   **Birks, H. J.** 1988. Long-term ecological change in the British uplands. In : Ecological Change in the Uplands : 37-56. Edited by M. B. Usher and D. B. A. Thompson. British Ecological Society. Blackwell Scientific Publications, Oxford.

19   **Birse, E. L. and Robertson, J. S.** 1976. Plant Communities and Soils of the Lowland and Southern Upland Regions of Scotland. The Macaulay Institute for Soil Research, Aberdeen.

20   **Bishop, W. W. and Coope, G. R.** 1977. Stratigraphical and Faunal Evidence for Lateglacial and Early Flandrian Environments in South-West Scotland. In : Studies in the Scottish Lateglacial Environment : 61-88. Edited by J. M. Gray and J. J. Lowe. Pergamon, Oxford.

22   **Borders Regional Council.** 1991. The Scottish Borders 2001 : Draft Structure Plan 1991. Department of Planning and Development, Borders Regional Council, Melrose.

23   **Brown, C. J., Shipley, B. M. and Bibby, J. S.** 1982. Soil Survey of Scotland : South-West Scotland. The Macaulay Institute for Soil Research, Aberdeen.

24   **Brown, L.** 1976. British Birds of Prey : 213-224. Collins, London.

25   **Brown, R. W.** (Edit.) 1991. Heather : Proceedings of the National Heather Convention.Seale Hayne Faculty, Polytechnic Southwest, Devon, UK.

26   **Buchanan, J. B., Schick, C. T., Brennan, L. A. and Herman, S. G.** 1988. Merlin predation on wintering Dunlins : hunting success and Dunlin escape tactics. Wilson Bulletin, 100 (1) : 108-118.

27   **Cadbury, C. J., Elliot, G. and Harbard, P.** 1988. Birds of Prey Conservation in the U.K. RSPB Conservation Review, No. 2 (1988). RSPB, Sandy.

28   **Cade, T. J.** 1982. The Falcons of the World. Comstock / Cornell University Press.

29   **Carlisle, A.** 1977. The impact of Man on the native pinewoods of Scotland. In : Native Pinewoods of Scotland : 70-77. Edited by R. G. H Bunce and J. N. R Jeffers. Natural Environment Research Council, Cambridge.

30   **Clarke, R.** 1987. Roosting Hen Harriers and Merlins. BTO News, 152 : 8-9.

31   **Clarke, R.** In press. Merlin *Falco columbarius* winter roosts and diet in Britain and Northern France. In : Biology and Conservation of Small Falcons. Proceedings of the 1991 Hawk and Owl Trust symposium.

32   **Coulson, J. C.** 1956. Mortality and egg production of the Meadow Pipit with special reference to altitude. Bird Study, 3 (2) : 119-132.

33   **Cowie, G. M.** 1989. The Galloway Forest Park - A History of Multi-Purpose Land Management. Voluntary paper for the 13th Commonwealth Forestry Conference, Rotorua, New Zealand.

34   **Cramp, S. & Simmons, K .E .L.** 1980. The Birds of the Western Palearctic : Vol 2 : 308-316. Oxford.

35   **Crick, H. Q. P.** In press. Trends in breeding success of Merlins in Britain from 1937 to 1989. In : Biology and Conservation of Small Falcons. Proceedings of the 1991 Hawk and Owl Trust symposium.

36   **Currie, F. A.** 1981. Observations on the breeding behaviour and association of Hen Harrier and Merlin on a North Wales heather moor. Nature in Wales, 17 (3) : 131-8.

37   **Currie, F. A. and Bamford, R.** 1981. Bird populations of sample pre-thicket forest plantations. Quarterly Journal of Forestry, 75 (2) : 75-82.

38   **Davies, J.** 1987. The History of the Red Deer of Galloway. Deer, Vol.7 (3) : 132-4. The British Deer Society.

39   **Dekker, D.** 1988. Peregrine falcon and merlin predation on small shorebirds and passerines in Alberta. Canadian Journal of Zoology, Vol. 66 : 925-928.

40   **Dementiev, G. P. and Gladkov, N. A.** 1951. Birds of the Soviet Union : Vol. 1. Sovyetskaya Nauka, Moscow. (English version published in 1966 by Israel Program for Scientific Translations, Jerusalem.)

41   **Department of Agriculture and Fisheries for Scotland.** 1989. Environmentally Sensitive Areas in Scotland : A First Report. DAFS, Edinburgh.

42   **Dickson, R. C.** 1973. A Merlin roost in Wigtownshire. Scot. Birds, Vol.7 : 288-292.

43   **Dickson, R. C.** 1983. Fledgling Merlins catching moths. Scot. Birds, Vol. 12 : 194.

44   **Dickson, R. C.** 1988. Habitat preferences and prey of Merlins in winter. British Birds,

81 (6) : 269-274.

45   **Dickson, R. C. and Watson, A. D.** 1974 . Early nesting Merlins in Galloway. Scottish Birds, Vol. 8 (3) : 194.

46   **Dorofeyev, A M. and Ivanovski, V. V.** 1980. The ecology of the Merlin (*Falco columbarius*) in Byelorussia. Vestnik Zoologii, 5 : 62-67.

47   **Ellis, P. M. and Okill, J. D.** 1990. Breeding ecology of the Merlin *Falco columbarius* in Shetland. Bird Study 37 (2) : 101-110.

48   **Everett, M.** 1991. The Controversial Hen Harrier. The Joseph Nickerson Reconciliation Project, Seventh Annual Report : 30-31.

49   **Feldsine, J. W. and Oliphant, L. W.** 1985. Breeding Behavior of the Merlin : The Courtship Period. Raptor Research, Vol. 19 (2/3) : 60-67.

50   **Felton, M. and Marsden, J.** 1990. Heather Regeneration in England and Wales : A Feasibility Study for the Department of the Environment. NCC, Peterborough.

51   **Forestry Commission.** 1950. National Forest Park Guides : Glen Trool. HMSO.

52   **Forestry Commission.** 1974. Wild Animals and Birds. In : FC Guide - Galloway Forest Park : 34-40. Edited by H. L. Edlin. HMSO, Edinburgh.

53   **Forestry Commission.** 1983. Census of Woodlands and Trees (South Scotland Conservancy) 1979-82. Forestry Commission, Edinburgh.

54   **Forestry Commission.** 1985. Guide to Upland Restocking Practice. Edited by A. J. Low. Forestry Commission Leaflet 84. HMSO, London.

55   **Forestry Commission.** 1986. The Forestry Commission & Conservation. Policy and Procedure Paper No. 4. Forestry Commission, Edinburgh.

56   **Forestry Commission.** 1989. Forest Landscape Design Guidelines. FC, Edinburgh.

57   **Forestry Commission.** 1990. Forest Nature Conservat. Guidelines. HMSO, London.

58   **Forestry Commission.** 1991a. Forestry Commission 70th Annual Report and Accounts, 1989-90. HMSO, London.

59   **Forestry Commission.** 1991b. Forestry Facts and Figures : 1989-90.

60   **Forestry Commission.** 1991c. Forests and Water Guidelines. HMSO, London.

61   **Forestry Commission.** 1991d. Woodland Grant Scheme : Grants and Procedures.

62   **Forestry Commission.** 1992. Forestry Facts and Figures : 1990-91.

63   **Fox, G. A.** 1964. Notes on the Western Race of the Pigeon Hawk. Blue Jay, 22:140-7.

64   **Fyfe, R. W. and Olendorff, R. R.** 1976. Minimizing the dangers of nesting studies to raptors and other sensitive species. Canadian Wildlife Service Occasional Paper 23.

65   **Galbraith, C. and Bates, M.** 1991. Regional Forest Strategies and bird conservation. In " Britain's Birds in 1989 - 90 " : 23-24. Edited by D. A. Stroud and D. Glue. Nature Conservancy Council and British Trust for Ornithology.

66   **Galushin, V. M.** 1981. Changes in population status and nest range distribution of falconiformes in the USSR since 1950. Raptor Research, 15 (1) : 4-11.

67   **Gibbons, D. W., Reid, J. B. and Chapman, R. A.** In press. The New Atlas of Breeding Birds in Britain and Ireland : 1988-1991. Poyser, London.

68   **Gilbert, J. M.** 1979. Hunting and Hunting Reserves in Medieval Scotland. John Donald, Edinburgh.

69   **Gladstone, H. S.** 1910. The Birds of Dumfries-shire. Witherby, London.

70   **Godwin, H.** 1956. The History of the British Flora. Cambridge University Press.

71   **Gordon, J. G.** (1920-25) The Birds of Wigtownshire. Manuscript.

72   **Gray, R.** 1871. The Birds of the West of Scotland. Murray, Glasgow.

73   **Gray, R. and Anderson, T.** 1869. The Birds of Ayrshire and Wigtownshire. Murray, Glasgow.

74   **Hård, I. and Enemar, A** 1980. The choice of prey and feeding by the Merlin *Falco columbarius* during the nestling period. Vår Fågelvörld, 39 : 25-34.

75   **Haworth, P. F. & Fielding, A.** 1988. Conservation and Management Implications of Habitat Selection in the Merlin *Falco columbarius* L. in the South Pennines, UK. Biological Conservation 46 : 247-260.

76   **Hayman, P.** 1985. The Birdwatcher's Pocket Guide. Mitchell Beazley, London.

77   **Heavisides, A.** 1987. British and Irish Merlin recoveries, 1911-1984. Ringing & Migration 8 (1) : 29-41.

78   **Heavisides, A.** 1992. Merlin study summary : 1991. Scottish Bird News, No. 25 : 4.

79   **Hewson, R. and Kolb, H. H.** 1974. The control of foxes in Scottish forests. Scottish Forestry, 28 : 272-282.

80   **Hewson, R. and Leitch, A. F.** 1983. The food of foxes in forests and on the open hill. Scottish Forestry, 37 : 39-50.

81   **Hibberd, B. G.** 1985. Restructuring of plantations in Kielder Forest District. Forestry, 58 (2) : 119-129.

82   **Highland Regional Council.** 1989. Caithness and Sutherland HRC Working Party : Summary Report and Land-Use Strategy. Highland Regional Council, Inverness.

83   **Hill, J. A.** 1983. Birds and Coniferous Plantations. Royal Forestry Society, Tring.

84   **HMSO.** 1985. Wildlife and Countryside (Amendment) Act 1985 : Chapter 31.

85   **Hodson, K. A.** 1976. The Ecology of Richardson's Merlins on the Canadian Prairies. Master of Science Thesis, University of British Columbia, Vancouver.

86   **Hogg, A.** 1983. Birds of Ayrshire. Glasgow University.

87   **Hudson, P. J.** 1984. Some effects of sheep management on heather moorlands in Northern England. In : The impact of agriculture on wildlife and semi-natural habitats : 143-149. Edited by D. Jenkins. ITE Symposium No. 13.

88   **Hudson, P. J.** 1986. Red Grouse : The Biology and Management of a Wild Gamebird. The Game Conservancy Trust, Fordingbridge.

89   **Hutchinson, C. D.** 1989. Birds in Ireland. Poyser, Calton.

90   **James, P .C.** 1988. Urban Merlins in Canada. British Birds, 81 : 274-277.

91   **James, P. C. and Smith, A. R.** 1987. Food habits of urban-nesting Merlins, Falco columbarius, in Edmonton and Fort Saskatchewan, Alberta. Canadian Field-Naturalist : 101 (4) : 592-594.

92   **Jardine, Sir W.** 1834. The Birds of Great Britain and Ireland. Vol 1. (Naturalists' Library : Ornithology). Allen and Co., London

93   **Jenkinson, R. D. S. & Gilbertson, D. D. 1984.** In the Shadow of Extinction. Nottinghamshire and Derbyshire County Council.

94   **Jones, V. J., Stevenson, A. C. and Battarbee, R. W.** 1989. Acidification of Lakes in Galloway, South West Scotland : A diatom and pollen study of the post-glacial history of the Round Loch of Glenhead. Journal of Ecology, 77 : 1-23.

95   **Knox, A. G.** 1990. The native pinewoods. In : The Birds of North-East Scotland. Edited by S. T. Buckland, M. V. Bell and N. Picozzi. NE Scotl. Bird Club, Aberdeen.

96   **Kovshar, A. F. and Rodionov, E. F.** 1984. Merlins nesting in the highlands of

Northern Tien-Shan. In : Proceedings of the 1983 Moscow Conference on Birds of Prey, Vol.1 (Ecology of Raptors) : 63-65. Edited by V. M. Galushin and V. E. Flint. Nauka, Moscow.

97   **Lack, P**. 1986. The Atlas of Wintering Birds in Britain and Ireland. Poyser, Calton.

98   **Laing, K.** 1985. Food habits and breeding biology of Merlins in Denali National Park, Alaska. Raptor Research, 19 (2/3) : 42-51.

99   **Lawrence, L. de K.** 1949. Notes on nesting pigeon hawks at Pimisi Bay, Ontario. Wilson Bulletin, 61 : 15-25.

100   **Lawton, J. H.** 1990. Red Grouse Populations and Moorland Management. The British Ecological Society. Field Studies Council, Shrewsbury.

101   **Leslie, R.** 1981. Birds of North East England Forests. Q. J. of Forestry, 75 : 153-158.

102   **Little, B. and Davison, M.** 1992. Merlins *Falco columbarius* using crow nests in Kielder Forest, Northumberland. Bird Study 39 : 13-16.

103   **Macintyre, D.** 1936. Wildlife of the Highlands. London.

104   **Mackenzie, W.** 1841. The History of Galloway From The Earliest Period To The Present Time, Volume 1. Nicholson, Kirkcudbright.

105   **McKerlie, P. H.** 1878. History of the Lands and their Owners in Galloway : Volume 4 of 5 volumes published 1870-79. William Paterson, Edinburgh.

106   **McVean, D. N. and Ratcliffe, D. A.** 1962. Plant Communities of the Scottish Highlands. HMSO, London.

107   **McWilliam, Rev. J. M.** 1936. The Birds of the Firth of Clyde. Witherby, London.

108   **Marquiss, M., Newton, I. and Ratcliffe, D. A.** 1978. The decline of the Raven *Corvus corax* in relation to afforestation in southern Scotland and northern England. Journal of Applied Ecology, 15 : 129-144.

109   **Marquiss, M., Ratcliffe, D. A. and Roxburgh, R.** 1985. The Numbers, Breeding Success and Diet of Golden Eagles (*Aquila chrysaetos*) in Southern Scotland in Relation to Changes in Land Use. Biological Conservation, 34 : 121-140.

110   **Matthews, J. R**. 1974. Plant Life. In : Forestry Commission Guide - Galloway Forest Park : 28-33. Edited by H.L.Edlin. HMSO, Edinburgh.

111   **Mead, C. J.** 1973. Movements of British raptors. Bird Study, 20 : 259-286.

112. **Mearns, R. and Newton, I.** 1988. Factors affecting breeding success of peregrines in south Scotland. Journal of Animal Ecology, 57 : 903-916.

113   **Meek, E. R.** 1988. The breeding ecology and decline of the Merlin *Falco columbarius* in Orkney. Bird Study, 35 : 209-218.

114   **Metereological Office.** 1989. The Climate of Scotland. HMSO. London.

115   **Mitchell, W. and Straker-Smith, P. D.** 1991. Living with Forestry. The Joseph Nickerson Reconciliation Project, Seventh Annual Report : 33-34.

116   **Moar, N. T.** 1969. Late Weichselian and Flandrian pollen diagrams from south-west Scotland. New Phytologist, 68 : 433-467.

117   **Moore, P. and Wilmott, A.** 1976. Prehistoric forest clearance and the development of peatlands in the uplands and lowlands of Britain. Proceedings of the Fifth International Peat Congress. Poznan, Poland (1976), 2 : 7-21.

118   **Moss, D.** 1979. Even-aged plantations as a habitat for birds. In " The ecology of even-aged forest plantations " : 413-427. Edited by E. D. Ford, D. C. Malcolm and J. Atterson. Institute of Terrestrial Ecology, Cambridge.

119   **Moss, D., Taylor, P. N. and Easterbee, N.** 1979. The Effects on Song-Bird

Populations of Upland Afforestation with Spruce. Forestry, 52 (2) : 129-147.

120 **Muirhead, G.** 1895. The Birds of Berwickshire : Volume 2. Douglas, Edinburgh.

121 **Murray, J. M.** 1935. An Outline of the History of Forestry in Scotland up to the End of the Nineteenth Century. The Scottish Forestry Journal, Vol. 49, Part 1 : 1-19.

122 **Nature Conservancy Council.** 1986. Nature Conservation and Afforestation in Britain. NCC, Peterborough.

123 **Newton, I.** 1984. Raptors in Britain - a review of the last 150 years. BTO News, 131.

124 **Newton, I.** 1986. The Sparrowhawk. Poyser, Calton

125 **Newton, I., Bogan, J., Meek, E. and Little, B.** 1982a. Organochlorine compounds and shell-thinning in British Merlins *Falco columbarius*. Ibis, 124 : 328-335.

126 **Newton, I., Davis, P. E. and Davis, J. E.** 1982b. Ravens and Buzzards in relation to sheep-farming and forestry in Wales. Journal of Applied Ecology, 19 : 681-706.

127 **Newton, I. and Haas, M. B.** 1984. The return of the Sparrowhawk. British Birds, 77 : 47-70.

128 **Newton, I. and Haas, M. B.** 1988. Pollutants in Merlin eggs and their effects on breeding. British Birds, 81 (6) : 258-269.

129 **Newton, I., Meek, E. R. and Little, B.** 1978. Breeding ecology of the Merlin in Northumberland. British Birds, 71 (9) : 376-398.

130 **Newton, I., Meek, E. R. and Little, B.** 1984. Breeding season foods of Merlins (*Falco columbarius*) in Northumbria. Bird Study, 31 : 49-56.

131 **Newton, I., Meek, E. R. and Little, B.** 1986a. Population and breeding of Northumbrian Merlins. British Birds, 79 (4) : 155-170.

132 **Newton, I. and Moss, D.** 1977. Breeding birds of Scottish pinewoods. In : Native Pinewoods of Scotland : 26-34. Edited by R. G. H. Bunce and J. N. R Jeffers. NERC. Institute of Terrestrial Ecology, Cambridge.

133 **Newton, I., Robson, J. E. and Yalden, D. W.** 1981. Decline of the Merlin in the Peak District. Bird Study, 28 : 225-234.

134 **Newton, I., Wyllie, I. and Mearns, R.** 1986b. Spacing of Sparrowhawks in relation to food abundance. Journal of Animal Ecology, 55 : 361-370.

135 **Nielsen, O. K.** 1986. Population Ecology of the Gyrfalcon in Iceland with comparative notes on the Merlin and Raven. Ph.D. thesis, Cornell University.

136 **O'Connor, R. J. and Shrubb, M.** 1986. Farming and Birds. Cambridge Univ. Press.

137 **Okill, J. D., Ginnever, J. A. & Jones, A.** 1980. Shetland's Merlins. Shetland Bird Report 1979 : 51-54.

138 **Oliphant, L. W.** 1974. Merlins -The Saskatoon Falcons. Blue Jay, 32 (3) : 140-147.

139 **Oliphant, L. W. and Haug, E.** 1985. Productivity, Population Density and Rate of Increase of an Expanding Merlin Population. Raptor Research, Vol. 19 (2/3) : 56-59.

140 **Oliphant, L. W. and McTaggart, S.** 1977. Prey Utilized by Urban Merlins. Canadian Field-Naturalist, Vol. 91 : 190-192.

141 **Oliphant, L. W. and Tessaro, S. V.** 1985. Growth Rates and Food Consumption of Hand-raised Merlins. Raptor Research Vol. 19 (2/3) : 79-84.

142 **Olsson, B. O.** 1980. Project Stenfalk. Svenska Naturskyddsföreningen, Stockholm.

143 **Orchel, J. H.** 1978. Notes on Merlins in Galloway. Unpublished report to the Forestry Commission, South Scotland Conservancy.

144 **Orchel, J. H.** 1981. Decline of the Merlin in Three Galloway Forests. Unpublished report to the Forestry Commission, South Scotland Conservancy.

145   **Orchel, J. H.** 1984. Plight of the Merlin.The Hawk Trust Ann. Rept., 1983, 13 : 17.

146   **Orchel, J. H. and Livingstone, J.** 1988. Merlin Conservation in Galloway. Unpublished report to the Forestry Commission, South Scotland Conservancy.

147   **Orchel, J. H. and Shawyer, C, R.** 1992. Barn Owl Conservation in Galloway. The Raptor, Volume 19 : 17-18. The Hawk and Owl Trust, London.

148   **Page, G. and Whitacre, D. F.** 1975. Raptor predation on wintering shorebirds. Condor 77 : 73-83.

149   **Parr, S. J.** 1991. Occupation of new conifer plantations by Merlins in Wales. Bird Study, 38 (2) : 103-111.

150   **Parr, S. J.** In press. Breeding ecology of the Merlin in Wales. In : Biology and Conservation of Small Falcons. Proceedings. of 1991 Hawk & Owl Trust symposium.

151   **Paton, E. R. and Pike, O.** 1929. The Birds of Ayrshire. Witherby, London.

152   **Peterken, G. F.** 1986. Commercial Forests and Woods - The Nature Conservation Opportunities. In : Forestry's Social and Environmental Benefits and Responsibilities : 53-63. Edited by R. J. Davies. Institute of Chartered Foresters.

153   **Peterken, G, F.** 1987. Natural features in the management of upland conifer forests. Proceedings of the Royal Society of Edinburgh, 93B : 223-234.

154   **Petty, S. J.** 1985a. A negative response of kestrels *Falco tinnunculus* to nestboxes in upland forests. Bird Study, 32 (3) : 194-195.

155   **Petty, S. J.** 1985b. Counts of some breeding birds in two recently afforested areas of Kintyre. Scottish Birds, 13 (8) : 258-262.

156   **Petty, S. J.** 1989. Goshawks : Their Status, Requirements and Management. Forestry Commission. HMSO, London.

157   **Petty, S. J. and Anderson, D.** 1986. Breeding by Hen Harriers *Circus cyaneus* on restocked sites in upland forests. Bird Study, 33 (3) : 177-178.

158   **Petty, S. J. and Anderson, D. I. K.** 1990. Goshawks in 1990. Unpublished report by Wildlife and Conservation Research Branch, Forestry Commission.

159   **Petty, S. J. & Avery, M. I.** 1990. Forest Bird Communities. FC, Edinburgh.

160   **Phillips, J.** 1991. Heather Burning and Management : 1911-1991. The Joseph Nickerson Reconciliation Project, Seventh Annual Report : 41-44.

161   **Picozzi, N.** 1975a. A study of the Carrion/Hooded Crow in north-east Scotland. British Birds, 68 : 409-419.

162   **Picozzi, N.** 1975b. Crow predation on marked nests. J. of Wildl. Manag., 39 : 151-5.

163   **Picozzi, N.** 1983. Growth and Sex of nestling Merlins in Orkney. Ibis,125: 377-382.

164   **Picozzi, N. and Catt, D. C. C.** 1988. Habitat requirements of black grouse in the Spey Valley. In : Land use in the River Spey catchment : 222-223. Edited by D. Jenkins. Aberdeen Centre for Land Use, University of Aberdeen.

165   **Ratcliffe, D. A. (Ed.)** 1977. A Nature Conservation Review : Vol. 1. Cambridge University Press, Cambridge.

166   **Ratcliffe, D. A.** 1980. The Peregrine Falcon. Poyser, Calton.

167   **Ratcliffe, D. A.** 1986a. The effects of afforestation on the wildlife of open habitats. In : Trees and wildlife in the Scottish uplands : 46-54. Edited by D. Jenkins. Institute of Terrestrial Ecology, Huntingdon.

168   **Ratcliffe, D. A.** 1986b. The Need for Retaining Open Ground Habitats for Wildlife. In : Forestry's Social and Environmental Benefits and Responsibilities : 32-38. Edited by R. J. Davies. Institute Of Chartered Foresters.

169 **Ratcliffe, D. A.** 1990. Bird life of mountain and upland. Cambridge Univ. Press.

170 **Ratcliffe, D. A. and Thompson, D. B. A.** 1988. The British uplands : their ecological character and international significance. In : Ecological Change in the Uplands : 9-36. Edit. by M. B. Usher and D. B. A. Thompson. Blackwell, Oxford.

171 **Ratcliffe, P. R.** 1987. The Future of the Red Deer of Galloway. Deer, Vol. 7, No. 3 : 134-136. The British Deer Society.

172 **Ratcliffe, P. R. and Petty, S. J.** 1986. The management of commercial forests for wildlife. In : Trees and wildlife in the Scottish uplands : 177-187. Edited by D. Jenkins. Institute of Terrestrial Ecology, Huntingdon..

173 **Rebecca, G. W.** 1989. Breeding performance of Merlins in North-East Scotland in 1988. The Raptor, Volume 17 : 13-14. The Hawk and Owl Trust, London.

174 **Rebecca, G. W.** 1990. Merlin *Falco columbarius.* In : The Birds of North-East Scotland. Edited by S. T. Buckland, M. V. Bell and N. Picozzi. North-East Scotland Bird Club, Aberdeen.

175 **Rebecca, G. W.** 1992. Merlins breeding in mature conifer plantation. North-East Scotland Bird Report 1991.

176 **Rebecca, G. W., Cosnette, B. L., Duncan, A., Picozzi, N. and Catt, D .C.** 1990. Hunting distance of breeding Merlins in Grampian indicated by ringed wader chicks taken as prey. Scottish Birds, Volume 16, Part 1 : 38-39.

177 **Rebecca, G. W., Cosnette, B. L., Hardey, J. J. C. and Payne, A. G.** 1992. Status, distribution and breeding biology of the Merlin in north-east Scotland, 1980-89. Scottish Birds : Vol. 16, No. 3 : 165-183.

178 **Rebecca, G. W. and Payne, A .G.** 1985. Breeding Merlins in North-East Scotland during 1983 and 1984. North-East Scotland Bird Report 1984 : 55-61.

179 **Rebecca, G. W., Payne, A. G. and Canham, M.** 1991. Merlins using man-made crow's nests. Scottish Bird News, No. 22 : 6.

180 **Reed, T .M.** 1985. Grouse Moors and Wading Birds. Game Conservancy Annual Report, 16 : 57-60.

181 **Ritchie, J.** 1920. The Influence of Man on Animal Life in Scotland. Cambridge University Press, Cambridge.

182 **Ritchie, R. J.** 1983. The results of raptor surveys along the Porcupine River, Alaska. Unpublished report for U.S. Fish and Wildlife Service, Endangered Species Office, Anchorage, Alaska.

183 **Roberts, E. L.** 1962. Merlins taking newly hatched passerines. Scot. Birds, 2 : 245.

184 **Roberts, J. L. and Green, D.** 1983. Breeding failure and decline of Merlins on a north Wales moor. Bird Study, 30 (3) : 193-200.

185 **Robertson, I. S.** 1982. The Origin of migrant Merlins on Fair Isle. British Birds, 75 : 108-111.

186 **Rose, L. N.** 1982. Breeding ecology of British pipits and their Cuckoo parasite. Bird Study, 29 (1) : 27-40.

187 **Rowan, W.** 1921-22. Observations on the breeding habits of the merlin. British Birds, 15 : 122-129, 194-202, 222-231, 246-253.

188 **Roxburgh, R.** 1988. In : Raptor Results 1987. Scottish Bird News No.10 : 7. Scottish Ornithologists' Club, Edinburgh.

189 **Royal Society for the Protection of Birds & Nature Conservancy Council.** 1991. Death by Design : Persecution of Birds of Prey and Owls in the UK 1979-1989.

190 **Rudebeck, G.** 1951. The choice of prey and modes of hunting of predatory birds with special reference to their selective effect. Oikos, 3 (2) : 200-231.

191   **Ruttledge, W.** 1985. Captive breeding of the European Merlin (*Falco columbarius aesalon*). Raptor Research : 19 (2/3) : 68-78.

192   **Schempf, P. F.** 1989. The Merlin in Alaska. The Raptor, Vol. 17 : 22-24.

193   **Schempf, P. F. and Titus, K.** 1988. Status of the Merlin (Falco c. columbarius) in Interior Alaska : 1987 Progress Report. U.S. Fish & Wildlife Service, Juneau, Alaska.

194   **Scott, D., Clarke, R. and Shawyer ,C. R.** 1991. Hen Harriers breeding in a tree-nest. Irish Birds. Vol. 4 (3) : 413-417.

195   **Scottish Office.** 1992. News Release (6th March/0395/92) : Lord Strathclyde Announces Major Expansion of ESAs in Scotland.

196   **Seel, D. C. and Walton, K. C.** 1979. Numbers of Meadow Pipits (*Anthus Pratensis*) on mountain farm grassland in N. Wales in the breeding season. Ibis, 121 : 147-164.

197   **Service, R.** 1903. The Diurnal and Ñocturnal Birds of the Solway Area. In : Transactions of Dumfriesshire and Galloway Natural History Society, XVII, Part 4.

198   **Sharrock, J. T. R.** 1976. The Atlas of Breeding Birds in Britain and Ireland. British Trust for Ornithology and Irish Wildbird Conservancy. Poyser, Berkhamsted.

199   **Shaw, G.** 1990. Timing and fidelity of breeding for Siskins *Carduelis spinus* in Scottish conifer plantations. Bird Study, 37 : 30-35.

200   **Shaw, G. and Dowell, A.** 1990. Barn Owl Conservation in Forests. Forestry Commission Bulletin 90. HMSO, London.

201   **Shaw, G. and Livingstone, J.** 1991. Goldfinches and other birds eating Sitka Spruce seed. BTO News 174 : 8-9.

202   **Sieg, C. H. and Becker, D. M.** 1990. Nest-site Habitat Selected by Merlins in Southeastern Montana. Condor, 92 : 688-694.

203   **Simms, E.** 1976. Woodland Birds. Collins, London.

204   **Sissons, J. B.** 1967. The Evolution of Scotland's Scenery. Oliver & Boyd, Edinburgh.

205   **Smith, A. R.** 1978. The Merlins of Edmonton. Alberta Naturalist, 8 : 188-191.

206   **Soutar, R. and Peterken, G.** 1989. Native Trees And Shrubs For Wildlife. Tree News, September 1989. The Tree Council, London.

207   **Staines, B. W.** 1986. Mammals of Scottish upland woods. In : Trees and wildlife in the Scottish uplands : 112-120. Edited by D. Jenkins. ITE, Huntingdon.

208   **Strathclyde Regional Council.** 1990. Strathclyde Consolidated Structure Plan Written Statement. Department of Physical Planning, Strathclyde R.C., Glasgow.

209   **Stroud, D. A.** 1987. A review of some consequences of open ground afforestation for upland birds. In : Forests For Britain : 29-39. British Association of Nature Conservationists.

210   **Stroud, D. A., Reed, T. M., Pienkowski, M. W. and Lindsay, R. A.** 1987. Birds, bogs and forestry : The peatlands of Caithness and Sutherland. NCC, Peterborough.

211   **Stroud, D. A., Reed, T. M. and Harding, N. J.** 1990. Do moorland breeding waders avoid plantation edges? Bird Study, 37 : 177-186.

212   **Temple, S. A.** 1972. Systematics and Evolution of the North American Merlins. The Auk, 89 : 325-338.

213   **Thom, V. M.** 1986. Birds in Scotland. Poyser, Calton.

214   **Thompson, D. B. A., Stroud, D. A. and Pienkowski, M. W.** 1988. Afforestation and upland birds : consequences for population ecology. In : Ecological Change in the Uplands : 237-259. Edited by M. B. Usher and D. B. A. Thompson. The British Ecological Society. Blackwell Scientific Publications, Oxford.

215 **Thompson, P. S., M. L. P. and D. B. A.** 1989. Cliff nesting Merlins in north-west Sutherland. Scottish Birds, Volume 15, Part 4 : 183-4.

216 **Titus, K. and Schempf. P. F.** 1990. Status of the Merlin *Falco c. columbarius* in Interior Alaska : 1989 Progress Report. US Fish & Wildlife Service, Juneau, Alaska.

217 **Trimble, S. A.** 1975. Habitat management series for unique or endangered species. Report No. 15 : Merlin *Falco columbarius*. US Department of the Interior : Bureau of Land Management, Denver, Colorado.

218 **Walker, G. J.** 1988. Inventory of Ancient, Long-Established and Semi-Natural Woodland (Provisional) : Wigtown District. Nature Conservancy Council, Edinburgh.

219 **Warkentin, I. G. and James, P. C.** 1988. Nest-site selection by urban Merlins. Condor 90 : 734-738.

220 **Warkentin, I. G. and James, P. C.** 1990. Winter Roost-site Selection by Urban Merlins (*Falco columbarius*). Raptor Research, 24 (1-2) : 5-11.

221 **Warkentin, I. G. and Oliphant, L. W.** 1990. Habitat use and foraging behaviour of urban merlins (*Falco columbarius*) in winter. J. Zool., London, 221 : 539-563.

222 **Warkentin, I. G., James, P. C. and Oliphant, L. W.** 1991. Influence of site fidelity on mate switching in urban-breeding merlins. The Auk, 108 : 294-302.

223 **Watson, A. and O'Hare, P. J.** 1979. Bird and mammal numbers on untreated and experimentally treated Irish bog. Oikos, 33 : 97-105.

224 **Watson, D.** 1972. Birds of Moor and Mountain. Scottish Academic Press, Edinburgh.

225 **Watson, D.** 1977. The Hen Harrier. Poyser, Berkhamsted.

226 **Watson, D.** 1981. Birdwatching in Galloway. Scottish Birds, 11 (6) : 188-193.

227 **Watson, D.** 1991. Hen Harriers breeding in a tree-nest : further comments. Irish Birds : Vol. 4, No. 3 : 418-420.

228 **Watson, J.** 1979. Food of Merlins nesting in young conifer forest. Bird Study, 26 : 253-258.

229 **Watt, H. B.** 1900. Scottish Forests and Woodlands in Early Historic Times. Annals of the Andersonian Naturalists' Society (Glasgow) 2, Part 2 : 89-107.

230 **Weir, D.** 1984. Whatever happened to the Merlin? Hawk Trust An. Rept., 13 : 18-20.

231 **Whitfield, D. P.** 1985. Raptor predation on wintering waders in southeast Scotland. Ibis, 127 : 544-558.

232 **Wiklund, C. G.** 1977. Breeding success of the Merlin *Falco columbarius* in an isolated subalpine birch forest. Vår Fågelvörld, 36 : 260-265.

233 **Wiklund, C. G.** 1979. Increased breeding success for Merlins *Falco columbarius* nesting among colonies of Fieldfares *Turdus Pilaris*. Ibis, 121 : 109-111.

234 **Williams, G. A.** 1981. The Merlin in Wales : breeding numbers, habitat and success. British Birds, 74 : 205-214.

ABOUT THE AUTHOR

Jack Orchel is a teacher, naturalist, writer and photographer specialising in northern forest ecosystems. He was born in Edinburgh in 1945 of Polish parentage. His interest in natural history stems from his youthful explorations of the Scottish Borders, Yorkshire Dales and North York Moors. In 1969 he was awarded an M.A. by the School of Slavonic Studies at London University where he read modern languages and international relations. Later he qualified as a teacher then trained in documentary film production at the London Film School. In 1977 he began a long-term study of birds of prey in the Galloway Forest Park and, as a Committee Member of the Hawk and Owl Trust, worked closely with landowners, farmers and foresters during the 1980s to promote Barn Owl and Merlin conservation in southern Scotland. Since 1988 he has coordinated the Trust's Scottish forest raptor project. He is Head of English and Drama at Gunnersbury Catholic School in London and is married with one daughter.